Psychoanalytic Think
Mental Health Settings

Marcus Evans

Routledge
Taylor & Francis Group

LONDON AND NEW YORK

First published 2021
by Routledge
2 Park Square, Milton Park, Abingdon, Oxon, OX14 4RN

and by Routledge
52 Vanderbilt Avenue, New York, NY 10017

Routledge is an imprint of the Taylor & Francis Group, an informa business

British Library Cataloguing-in-Publication Data
A catalogue record for this book is available from the British Library

Library of Congress Cataloging-in-Publication Data
Library of Congress Cataloging-in-Publication Data

Names: Evans, Marcus, 1961—author.
Title: Psychoanalytic thinking in mental health settings / Marcus Evans.
Description: New York, NY: Routledge, 2021. | Includes bibliographical references and
  index. | Summary: "This book demonstrates the use of psychoanalytic thinking in front
  line mental health settings and aims to make available an approach to working with
  emotional and mental disturbance to a wide range of clinicians within psychiatric and
  other mental health settings. Rooted in the author's extensive clinical experiences, the
  approach explored in this book applies psychoanalytic thinking and discusses this in
  relation to the mental health conditions regularly encountered in psychiatric settings,
  such as Schizophrenia, Manic Depression, Psychotic Depression, Anorexia, Deliberate Self
  Harm and Personality Disorder. The book therefore provides valuable and practical ways
  of working with these difficult, complex, and problematic conditions. It further makes
  sense of the relationships and emotions encountered when working in these settings
  and introduces possibilities for more effective and rewarding ways of working, including
  a model of support through supervision, reflective practice, and clinical discussion.
  Illustrated by clinical examples from more than four decades of experience in the field,
  this book is ideal for the interested mental health practitioner"—provided by publisher.
Identifiers: LCCN 2020022205 (print) | LCCN 2020022206 (ebook) | ISBN 9780367567361
  (hardback) | ISBN 9780367567385 (paperback) | ISBN 9781003099192 (ebook)
Subjects: LCSH: Psychotherapy. | Mental health personnel and patient. | Psychoanalytic
  interpretation. | Mental health services.
Classification: LCC RC480.5 .E85 2021 (print) | LCC RC480.5 (ebook) | DDC
  616.89/14--dc23
LC record available at https://lccn.loc.gov/2020022205
LC ebook record available at https://lccn.loc.gov/2020022206

ISBN: 978-0-367-56736-1 (hbk)
ISBN: 978-0-367-56738-5 (pbk)
ISBN: 978-1-003-09919-2 (ebk)

Typeset in Times New Roman
by Deanta Global Publishing Services, Chennai, India

Psychoanalytic Thinking in Mental Health Settings

This book demonstrates the use of psychoanalytic thinking in front-line mental health settings and aims to make an approach to working with emotional and mental disturbance available to a wide range of clinicians within psychiatric and other mental health settings.

Rooted in the author's extensive clinical experiences, the approach explored in this book applies psychoanalytic thinking and discusses this in relation to the mental health conditions regularly encountered in psychiatric settings, such as Schizophrenia, Manic Depression, Psychotic Depression, Anorexia, Deliberate Self Harm, and Personality Disorder. The book therefore provides valuable and practical ways of working with these difficult, complex, and problematic conditions. It further makes sense of the relationships and emotions encountered when working in these settings and introduces possibilities for more effective and rewarding ways of working, including a model of support through supervision, reflective practice, and clinical discussion.

Illustrated by clinical examples from more than four decades of experience in the field, this book is ideal for the interested mental health practitioner.

Marcus Evans is a psychoanalyst and former consultant psychotherapist at the Tavistock & Portman NHS Foundation Trust. After qualifying there as a psychotherapist, he was appointed Head of Nursing and subsequently Associate Clinical Director of the Adult & Adolescent Departments, 2011–2015. He has given outreach courses to front-line staff in several Mental Health Trusts, including Camden and Islington, the Bethlem and Maudsley, and Broadmoor. His other book, *Making Room for Madness in Mental Health*, was published by Routledge in 2016.

This book is dedicated to my wife and family for all their support and encouragement in writing this book.

Contents

Foreword   viii
Preface   xi
Acknowledgements   xii
Background   xiii

1 Introduction   1

2 Theory in practice   8

3 Supervision and consultation: Tuning in to psychotic communications in front-line mental health settings   22

4 Therapeutic and anti-therapeutic factors in therapeutic relationships   34

5 Psychoanalytic understanding of depression and suicidal risk   50

6 Psychotherapeutic work with emotionally unstable personality disorder   66

7 Tuning in to psychotic communication on a psychiatric intensive care unit   82

8 Therapeutic work with treatment-resistant patients   94

9 The contribution of psychoanalytic perspectives on the patient's relationship with their bodies   107

10 Social systems and social defence   121

Index   139

Foreword

When starting out as a trainee in psychiatry, I was struck by the impact my patients had on me—how frequently the encounters of the day could not be easily let go of when I got home. My previous work in general medicine and surgery had exposed me to many distressed people and families struggling with cancer or severe disease—their distress and suffering was obvious and often painful. But the experience of my first six months in psychiatry felt different. Whereas the patients I'd encountered in medicine were likely to be of my grandparent's generation, in psychiatry many were close to me in age. It was easier, in my mid-twenties, to identify with their distress. But that wasn't all. In psychiatry the "pathology" one is trying to grapple with, rather than residing in the lungs or liver, is at the heart of what makes the person: their feelings, relationships, experiences, thoughts, and personality—and understanding this psychopathology often leaves the professional feeling exposed and vulnerable.

The distress of someone with persistent suicidal feelings—or someone who is convinced that their thoughts are being controlled by an alien force—need, at some level, to be experienced by the clinician in order for the person to feel understood and to be helped. To do so is inherently unsettling. The patient with mania, perhaps treated on a "section," places any psychiatrist, but most of all, the inexperienced trainee, in a challenging position. The patient does not feel ill—on the contrary, he or she might be feeling better than ever—and yet the team is restricting the individual's freedoms. Mania from the textbooks sounded exciting: the reality was far more unsettling, not least because the patient with mania seemed uncannily equipped to see through one's defences and identify exactly what might get under your skin.

The substance of what I was being taught in psychiatric training, on diagnosis, classification, phenomenology, treatment, and prognosis, was essential to make some sense of the chaos many of my patients were living with and leaving me feeling. There were procedural tasks which had to be learned about mental health law, and handling risk. But the mainstream psychiatry which made up most of my training was not enough. It did not address the issues which left me feeling unsettled after a day's work. The playwright Joe Orton had one of his characters say:

"you can't be rational in an irrational world—it's irrational." This was how the approach I was learning (and which I practice and research today) felt.

My exposure to psychoanalytic thinking came in dribs and drabs—much of it written in fairly impenetrable language. Some of the formal psychoanalytic teaching we had was easy to dismiss as it seemed inaccessible and far-fetched. But in clinical supervisions with psychoanalysts, and in clinical seminars where complex cases were being discussed, the psychoanalytic perspective often hit home. The patient's difficulties, which weren't being captured by diagnostic labels, were being identified in a psychoanalytic formulation which often seemed creative and to provide space for a different kind of explanation from that provided by the phenomenological approach used in psychiatry. The recognition that hidden, unacceptable feelings of rage or envy within a patient could manifest in an entirely different way could suddenly open up a new understanding. Perhaps most important was the understanding that the feelings which patients elicited in me were important to recognise and gave insights into their inner world.

This book provides insights into these building blocks of psychoanalytic thought—the unconscious defence mechanisms, transference and counter-transference, in clear language and with great clinical wisdom. It also makes clear the importance of psychoanalytic process in routine mental health care—a respect for boundaries, the importance of reflection and supervision.

These insights are more important now than ever. Mental health services have become, over the last two decades, increasingly obsessed with risk posed by people with severe mental illness, and this has been at the expense of providing a good therapeutic environment. We are pressured by bed closures, by the Care Quality Commission, by audit and quality improvement to relentlessly improve *processes* of care. Forms must be completed, risk assessments done, outcomes measured, mandatory training completed, and if psychological treatment is provided at all, it must, at all costs, be brief. Despite all the energy which seems to have been poured into creating a more accountable system of care, patients' experiences have not improved. Indeed, some of the innovations in recent years have led to a reduction in that most essential quality of all health systems—continuity of care. We have also seen a great increase in the use of coercion—the in-patient units which still exist virtually only admit people against their will. These issues have had an adverse impact on staff—mental health services have many unfilled posts, there is a recruitment and retention problem, and many mental health trusts are struggling to maintain safe levels of staffing.

Increasingly, my feeling is that it is not only that clinical staff in mental health services need the insights psychoanalytic thinking can bring in order to provide more compassionate care but also that the way in which services are designed, and what they may represent to the people who use and rely upon them, also requires such understanding.

Marcus Evans's background as a psychiatric nurse and psychoanalyst is unusual—and imbues the book with the direct and practical clinical insights which I valued so much in my psychiatric training. I wish I had had the companionship of this book then.

Professor Matthew Hotopf, CBE FRCPsych FMedSci
Vice Dean of Research, Institute of Psychiatry
Psychology and Neuroscience
Director, NIHR Biomedical Research Centre at the Maudsley

Preface

In this important book which follows his early work entitled *Making Room for Madness in Mental Health* (Evans, 2016), the author continues to explore different ways psychoanalytic ideas can be of use in mental health settings. The basic premise is the same: listen to the patient and try to formulate their situation in ways that make sense to them and to us.

Severe mental illness is frightening and perplexing. Not only is it irrational and emotionally charged but it draws us into a strange world which can threaten our own mental equilibrium. It is difficult to begin to spend time listening to patients unless one has a framework that makes sense of their experience and allows one to empathise with their suffering. Psychoanalysis is one such framework which the author found provided him with an orientation when he came up against disturbing encounters.

He began his career working as a psychiatric nurse in a large mental hospital and felt that he lacked the tools to help him cope with his work. He went on to train as a psychotherapist and then as a psychoanalyst so that he could return and help the many who are as bewildered as he was. The vignettes in this book show that it is possible to explore and make sense of the patient's experiences, both of their illness and of the way others respond to it. In this way a psychoanalytic approach can complement traditional psychiatry based on diagnosis and drug treatment. It can foster a humane atmosphere by providing ways of understanding the patient's illness. It encourages the staff to talk to the patients and listen to them as people and not just cases that need to be dealt with. All those who work in the field of mental health will find this book interesting and useful, and the interested layman will find a fascinating introduction to the world of mental illness.

John Steiner (born 1934) is a psychoanalyst, author and trainer at the British Psychoanalytical Society. Steiner, a "prolific London post-Kleinian," is best known for his conceptions of the "pathological organisation" or the "psychic retreat" between the paranoid-schizoid and the depressive positions. His book, *Psychic Retreats*, describes a treatment methodology for patients with complex defence mechanisms that are difficult to treat with conventional psychoanalysis.

Acknowledgements

I want to thank Annie Peskin, Dr. Rink Alam, and Sue Evans for their invaluable help in critiquing and editing this book; Dr John Steiner for writing the preface and his ongoing support through supervision; and Professor Matthew Hotopf for writing the foreword. I have always believed that psychoanalysis and psychiatry need one another, even if their interdependence sometimes goes unacknowledged. I hope the book will help develop understanding between these disciplines in the hope that this will improve the care of patients with serious mental health problems.

I would also like to thank all my trainees, colleagues, supervisors, teachers, mentors, and, last but by no means least, my patients who have taught me so much over many years.

Background

In this book, I hope to illustrate the value of psychoanalytic thinking using clinical vignettes of work with staff in mental health teams. I hope it will show how even the most intractable of patients can be supported to develop healthier ways of managing their difficulties, as well as revealing the ways in which staff members working with this patient group can find the work both professionally rewarding and personally creative. When staff are empowered to understand the most bewildering presentations and symptoms, their curiosity for the work is stimulated and their skill in the work grows. Higher morale, lower burnout, and improved clinical outcomes are the result. In this book I will argue for the place of psychoanalytic thinking in the treatment of patients with long-term mental conditions to run alongside other approaches. I will also demonstrate the use of psychoanalytic approaches when thinking about the management and care of patients with chronic mental illness and or personality disorders.

I trained as a mental health nurse in a large psychiatric hospital in the early 1980s. However, my training failed to give me any model for understanding patients' bizarre presentations. The medical treatments available acted to dampen down the threatening influence of acute psychotic states. The accompanying nursing care attempted to provide a safe environment that cared for acutely disturbed patients in risky states of mind. Although we offered one-to-one nursing and sometimes therapeutic groups, there was no theoretical model of the mind to underpin this work. In the absence of a way to think about the meaning of patients' communications, these therapeutic interventions tended to be driven by the wish to remind the patient of external reality. The implicit belief seemed to be since the psychotic patient had withdrawn from reality, reminding them of reality might shake them out of their psychosis. Meanwhile, we believed a person with personality disorder was dominated by infantile and therefore thoughtless states of mind and so they needed to be reminded of the need for more mature thinking and action.

Although this approach was compelling to us, the staff, it failed to open up a dialogue with the patient about the nature of their difficulties. I am not against spelling out reality or reminding the patient that a more mature approach would be helpful; this is necessary from time to time. However, presumably the patient would live in the world of reality or develop more mature ways of thinking or behaving if they could; indeed, much of the time the patient would agree they needed to stop thinking or acting in these ways. However, the patient's good intentions often broke down when the symptoms returned, leading to feelings of guilt and failure. When listening to mental health professionals present their work, I am often struck by the difficulty of finding a common language both professional and patient can speak. The psychotic patient communicates via psychotic symptoms while the personality-disordered patient communicates through action. More often than not, both forms of communication are being employed. It can feel as if they are talking different emotional languages.

I was introduced to psychoanalytic thinking by a consultant psychotherapist who used to run an in-patient ward group. I was impressed by the attempt to think about patients' communications as things which could potentially be understood. Encouraged by the consultant psychotherapist, I started to read Melanie Klein. I found Klein offered a lens for thinking about the patients' internal worlds and I was intrigued by her descriptions of the role of unconscious phantasy in mental life. Her writing also provided a model for thinking about the relationship between the patient and the professional in terms of "the transference." In this book, using clinical examples taken from my own psychotherapy work with patients and from my supervision of mental health staff, I hope to demonstrate the relevance and helpfulness of psychoanalytic thinking in mental health settings.

Chapter 1

Introduction

Nurses from a mental health ward presented a patient, who had been admitted under a Mental Health Act Section, in a psychotic state. The patient had been preaching in a shopping centre and assaulted anyone who failed to acknowledge he was Christ. Brought into hospital by the police as he would not come voluntarily, once on the ward the patient complained that he was being locked inside an airless oven and feared he would asphyxiate and die.

When listening to patients in psychiatric settings, we need to tune in to the patient at different levels, both concrete and symbolic. At a concrete level, this patient is telling us that he feels threatened and believes his life is in danger. But what is being conveyed at a symbolic level by this concrete communication? My own thought listening to the nurses was that the patient was worried the staff were going to try to kill off his psychotic self. If my idea was correct, then in many ways, the patient is right. The psychiatric services want to help the patient return to a world of shared reality. I often think that we are working at cross-purposes with the patient. The patient defends himself from the depressing reality of his situation as a man with a psychiatric condition by moving into a delusion that he is Christ, a powerful man at the centre of a religion, who has healing powers. Patients often retreat into psychotic states of mind because they don't believe they can bear the pain involved in facing reality. Psychotic states of mind can be extremely destructive, denying important aspects of reality and causing harm to relationships with self and/or others. However, the mental health services' ambition to return the patient to the sane world may be experienced as a threat, as this involves attempts to crush the state of mind that the patient believes protects him from catastrophic breakdown. The diagnoses and active interventions employed by psychiatry can be experienced by the patient as more concerned with keeping them quiet and preventing the ward, the community, and society in general from being disturbed by their mental state.

Current mental health policy can be described as aimed at two main groups—individuals with severe mental illness, typically psychotic disorders like schizophrenia, and people with so-called "common mental disorders," such as depression and anxiety.

Policy has tended to focus services for the former groups in secondary mental health care, with an emphasis on risk—i.e. prevention of harm to self and others. Secondary mental health services have been under great pressure, with cuts in bed numbers and a tendency for care to become increasingly procedural and coercive (with massive increases in rates of involuntary admission). There is a danger that as pressure for these services builds, staff become more mechanistic in response to the suffering of the patients they treat.

Meanwhile, for common mental disorders like anxiety and depression, policy has increasingly focused on the provision of brief therapies such as cognitive behavioural therapy (CBT) offered by healthcare professionals often with limited training, delivered within Increasing Access to Psychological Treatment (IAPT) services. However, these primary care services can fail to address more chronic underlying problems in the patients they see.

The reality is that people with chronic and/or acute mental disorders usually have long-standing difficulties caused by risk factors including disrupted parenting, childhood abuse, social disadvantage, and trauma. This often causes them problems in settling into education, staying in employment, and forming stable long-term relationships. Individuals may suffer from a range of difficulties, including psychosis, personality disorders, depression, anxiety, post-traumatic stress disorder, self-harm, and substance misuse.

Such individuals need an in-depth understanding of their psychopathology and any treatment needs to take account of the seriousness and long-term damage such early-life experiences can cause. The experience of disrupted relationships in the past with parents, carers, and authority figures can be unconsciously repeated in care settings and it is all too easy for services to become defeated or disengaged as the patient's difficulties are deemed too intractable to be helped.

Psychoanalytic thinking offers just such an in-depth understanding for mental health practitioners, as well as providing long-term treatment for some patients. Not everyone will benefit from intensive psychotherapies, but psychoanalytic understanding and formulations can help clinical services—both in primary and secondary mental health care—to provide humane and thoughtful care.

Psychoanalytically informed work is interested in the complexity of human relationships and how an individual's development is affected by their past. The approach looks in detail at how patterns of relating are repeated, including in therapeutic settings. Key to this is understanding the obstacles to engagement and resistance to recovery. It is concerned with gaining an understanding of a person's disturbed and disturbing state of mind and working collaboratively with the patient. Rather than just dealing with a crisis, the emphasis is on gaining an understanding of the person's self-defeating patterns of behaviour.

Serious and enduring mental illness and/or personality disorder can make it hard for patients to face the extent of their difficulties and suffering. This can lead to a withdrawal from the world of shared emotions and into psychotic and delusional thinking. Indeed, patients in disturbed states of mind often feel dislocated from the family of ordinary human experience. Mental health professionals need to spend time with these patients in order to understand their experiences. This can be challenging as it involves allowing themselves to be affected by the fragmented communications and delusional worlds of their patients. Ordinary communication may be stripped of its symbolic value and of all emotional significance. This creates a gulf that leaves mental health professionals and patients' relatives feeling alienated and deprived of meaningful contact with the patient. The danger is that mental health professionals respond by becoming mechanistic in their thinking, leaving patients feeling they—and their damaged minds—are being kept at a distance. Indeed, mental health reports on patients' views often state that staff spend more time in the office than face-to-face engaging with them.

Alternatively, mental health professionals may try to eradicate psychotic signs and symptoms with aggressive doses of anti-psychotic medication. This is an attitude which can be encouraged by a shortage of beds and the factory mentality which demands that patients be discharged as quickly as possible. Discharge is often based on the absence of positive symptoms, rather than an assessment of the patient's overall well-being. However, even though psychotic states of mind are serious and may cause considerable suffering and pain to patients and their relatives, the psychosis cannot be fully eradicated with drugs as it represents an aspect of the patient's mind. This is not to say that psychosis and its side effects should not be treated medically; the danger is, rather, that professionals may further persecute patients by giving the impression that aspects of their minds are intolerable. This intolerance of damage mirrors the patient's difficulty in mourning the loss of the ideal self.

In his paper "Mourning and Melancholia," Freud (1917) described the way the depressed patient internalises the original object (e.g. the parent) as a way of avoiding the pain of separation and loss. The object then becomes part of the individual's mind, where it is criticised and attacked for failing to be the ideal. In cases of melancholia, aggression is directed towards the self and away from the external object who has failed them. The self is omnipotently to blame for everything, and there is no attempt to differentiate between realistic or unreasonable guilt. This often develops into a sado-masochistic relationship between the ego and the super ego where the ego is blamed for everything. As Freud (1917) pointed out, the masochistic state of mind conceals considerable grandiosity and narcissism. The Masochism of the Melancholic says: "I am to blame for everything" because "I am responsible for everything" and no one else's contribution, including the contribution of reality, makes any difference. Hence the victim of childhood sexual abuse may appropriately feel guilty about the perverse aspects of their own sexuality, which they feel degrades them. However, as a child victim they are not responsible for their abuser's behaviour (Steiner, 2018). I suspect the repetitive nature of these patients' cycle of recovery and relapse is driven by a need to avoid mourning the loss of the ideal version of the self. The capacity to mourn one's previously held beliefs and identities is an essential aspect of a healthy mental life. Those that cannot adapt to feedback gained from external reality are doomed to fail because they cannot learn from experience.

Depressive experiences in psychotic patients are often difficult for patients to stay with (and for staff to witness). Indeed, feelings of despair about the extent of the damage can lead to a manic wish for a God-like figure that can cure all problems, reminding us of the patient I began this chapter with, who was found in a shopping centre claiming he was Christ. Patients often locate their fear of, and contempt for, their own psychological disturbance in other patients, whom they then see as disturbing. This allows them to adopt a superior attitude towards this aspect of their own mind, which they now see as residing in somebody else. They then try to control the "others" that are now believed to contain the damaged aspects of the self. Psychoanalytic thinking can help clinicians understand the way aspects of the self may be located in external objects, including themselves as members of staff.

Serious mental illness and personality disorder can deprive people of ordinary experiences, as their condition interferes with their ability to realise their dreams and aspirations. This can leave them feeling that they have been left on the margins of life, as indeed they often are. References to depressing states of mind therefore often accompany patients' presentations. Even patients in manic states of mind talk about feelings of emptiness and fearfulness of catastrophic events, for example, nuclear explosions, as part of their presentation.

Registering these depressing experiences about the damage done by their illness and psychosis can prove hard for staff and patients as attention is more often drawn to the bizarre aspects of the presentation, such as manic mood or the real risk to self and others. Indeed, feelings of despair can lead to a manic wish for a figure who can cure all problems often represented by delusions of identification with a powerful figure, for example, God, Jesus, Mohammed, etc., but can also manifest as a child-like belief that the staff can offer a magical cure. This attitude can quickly flip over into grievance when staff fail to "cure" the patient of their difficulties.

In addition to experiencing feelings of anxiety, loss, and despair, patients who become aware of the extent of their difficulties are also prone to feelings of humiliation. Dependence upon professionals and the inevitable imbalance of power between the patient and the perceived authority can highlight patients' feelings of inferiority. The fact that mental health professionals are required to assess the patient's state of mind and functioning can also exacerbate feelings of being looked down on, judged, and shamed. Professionals need to be sensitive to these feelings and, whenever possible, help to support patients as well as manage the risks they pose. When professionals act in ways that are insensitive to the patients' shame and humiliation, this may exacerbate historical feelings of resentment and unfairness in relation to authority figures. If these issues are not understood, they can become the locus of a grievance between the patient and the professional, which undermines the therapeutic relationship that is central to the process of recovery.

The patients' communications and actions can have a disturbing effect on mental health professionals and can provoke them into reacting by trying to control the patient's thinking or behaviour. Although at times actions taken by staff are appropriate and necessary, they may also be driven by a wish to curtail provocative or disturbing elements of the patient's mind. Tuning into different levels of communication is a strain and may pull the staff member's mind in several different directions at the same time. It is common for staff in mental health settings to leave work experiencing a headache, or feeling a need to go and have a drink. Staff also say they sometimes dream about their patients as they become affected by the disturbing nature of their work.

In his book *Second Thoughts* (1967), Bion described a patient in a lift who pushed the button for two floors at the same time as he believed he could go to two places concurrently. In my experience, this sense of having one's thinking pulled in two directions—psychotic and non-psychotic—is common. It is important to note that psychoanalysts often use the term "psychotic" to describe psychotic mechanisms that operate in a broad range of mental states and presentations. This definition would encompass a mental activity that would not be described as psychotic from a psychiatric point of view. Although psychotic patients often deny their illness and complain they are being admitted against their will, they also fear being left to struggle with their psychosis on their own, without support. Ultimately, it is incumbent upon staff to try to understand both the disruptive and the destructive elements in their patients' thinking. Without this, there is a risk that the underlying meanings of communications are lost, ignored, or crushed.

The mental health system is under enormous pressure as the reduction in the number of hospital beds has meant that only acutely ill patients are admitted to the hospital for relatively short periods of time. Staff are therefore expected to contain patients in disturbed states of mind in community settings. The current emphasis on services to manage risk in the community assumes that risk assessment is accurate. However, mental illness is, by nature, unpredictable and mental health professionals cannot assess patients' behaviour with any degree of certainty. This leaves mental health professionals in the community managing large amounts of anxiety about blame, when patients act out against themselves or others in a violent or damaging way. The pressure on in-patient beds means that wards are full of acutely ill patients, a high percentage of whom will be detained under a Mental Health Act, often against their will. Wards have to be locked to prevent absconding, which creates a custodial atmosphere. The high level of disturbance on wards means that staff are dealing with a non-stop experience of their patients' disturbed states of mind. Physical and verbal violence towards staff is common and, in many ways, accepted as being part of the job. Patients in these wards are often discharged as soon as they show any sign of "health," and this early discharge deprives the patients of the opportunity to consolidate their improved condition by undertaking therapeutic and occupational programmes. It also deprives the ward of an opportunity to work with the patient in an improved state where healthier aspects of their personality may be supported and nurtured. This cycle can lead to a revolving door syndrome, as early discharge results in relapse and readmission, which can be demoralising for staff and patients alike.

Relationship with management

Lord Francis's report on North Staffs outlined the way financial preoccupations provoked a top-down management system designed to control budgets. These systems are good at controlling resources but not so good at providing feedback back up the chain. Thus, anxieties about the quality of clinical services tend to reside with clinical staff while management become removed from front-line concerns. Pressure on services and high levels of disturbance in the patient population can also lead to high numbers of serious, untoward incident enquiries. Learning from experience is an important part of good institutional practice. However, anxiety about the management of risk can influence the culture of these enquiries and they shift from a wish to learn from experience into a need to attribute blame. These conditions can create an unhelpful "them and us" situation between management and staff. Good morale is one of the key ingredients of good mental health care. However, when hard-pressed staff in Mental Health Trusts feel unappreciated or mistrusted by management, it can lead to demoralisation. This, in turn, can have a damaging effect on the quality of clinical services as morale suffers. Mental health professionals need to feel that the management understand the conflicts and difficulties inherent in their work.

Support for clinical staff

Ef   work depends on professionals' willingness to allow
th   le to patients' suffering, while still maintaining a pro-
fe   Vhen the staff are functioning well, they can take in and
empathise with   nt's situation, while not becoming either overwhelmed or over-identified—two responses that can lead to clinical difficulties. When the latter situation arises, the professional's anxiety may become abnormally high, *leading to anti-therapeutic behaviour in relation to the patient.* Professionals may attempt to cure the patient through "heroic" efforts, exhibiting a therapeutic zeal underpinned by a wish to eliminate disturbance. Alternatively, the professional may attempt to distance him/herself from the patient, who is then felt to be pervaded by damaged and damaging states of mind. When this happens, the professional may develop a hard external skin designed to keep the patient and his or her disturbance at a safe distance, giving the patient the feeling they are being treated with cruel indifference.

In order to develop and maintain a balanced approach, clinical staff need settings, structures, and a theoretical model that can help them digest the anxiety and pain involved in developing therapeutic relationships with such disturbing and disturbed patients. Support needs to be provided through supervision, reflective practice, and clinical discussion. These aspects of staff support should be perceived not as luxuries but as part of responsible, professional practice. In such settings, professionals find opportunities to separate from their identification with the patient and restore their objective clinical approach, while others are helped to reflect on hardened attitudes in the interests of becoming more emotionally available. While psychoanalysis is neither an appropriate nor a practical treatment for most patients with a severe and enduring mental illness, it does offer a model for staff to think about psychotic states of mind. As Richard Lucas used to say, it helps us "tune into the psychotic wavelength" thereby providing a model for thinking about the anxieties that drive us "out of our minds." Psychoanalytic thinking and insight provide a model for taking account of the unconscious forces that operate within therapeutic relationships, and thus for understanding the meaning of symptoms. Clinical discussion about the nature of the relationships between staff and patients, including enactments, can throw light on the clinical issues underlying the patient's presentation and ways of relating. This in return can reduce the risk of thoughtless action in both patients and their carers.

Thinking psychoanalytically provides staff with a language for describing psychological interactions that take place within all therapeutic relationships and for articulating their experiences with patients in a thoughtful and considered way. It helps professionals to see a different dimension of the patient through transference and counter-transference dynamics in the therapeutic relationship, thus providing a bridge between the more traditional psychiatric model and the patient's actual personality and current state of mind. Above all, it encourages professionals to remain curious about their patients—about their functioning over time and in all the different areas of their lives.

In conclusion, I quote Edna O'Shaughnessy (2016), a British psychoanalyst, who argues that "the psychoanalytic method does not keep insanity out of view but tries to offer madness a habitat and human understanding."

References

Bion, W. R. (1967). Differentiation of the psychotic from the non-psychotic personalities. In *Second thoughts: Selected papers on psychoanalysis* (pp. 43–64). New York, NY: Jason Aronson.

Freud, S. (1917). Mourning and melancholia. In *The standard edition of the complete psychological works of Sigmund Freud*, Volume 14, (pp. 237–259). London: Hogarth Press.

O'Shaughnessy, E. (2016). Foreword. In M. Wadell and J. Catty (Eds.), *Making room for madness in mental health: The psychoanalytic understanding of psychotic communication* (pp. xxi–xxiii). London: Karnac Books.

Steiner, J. (2018). The trauma and disillusionment of Oedipus. *International Journal of Psychoanalysis*, *99*(3), 555–568.

Chapter 2

Theory in practice

Freud's structural theory of the mind

Freud (1923) described three areas of the mind that work in dynamic relation to one another: Id, Ego, and Super Ego. The *id* is part of the mind that contains drives and unconscious phantasies associated with the drives. These unconscious impulses often become visible through people's actions or mistakes, like forgetting the birthday of someone you are annoyed with, or giving oneself away by slips of the tongue. The *ego* is the part of the mind that integrates perceptions and thinks about the nature of the individual's relationship with the internal and the external world, while the *super ego* represents internalised rules and regulations.

Freud thought of the ego as the place in the mind that serves two masters. The instinctual forces emanating from the *id* demand satisfaction, but the satisfactions need to be achieved in the context of an internalised social environment represented by the *super ego*. In this way the ego has to deal with conflict and tolerate frustrations associated with the task of balancing instinctual desires in a social context. The ego needs to be able to bear a certain amount of psychic pain in order to tolerate the inherent anxiety and conflicts involved in being in a relationship with others. It is important to stress that we all employ psychic defences in order to protect the ego from overwhelming psychological pain and anxiety. Indeed, these psychic defences are essential for healthy functioning. When the ego is exposed to too much pain it either causes a collapse in functioning or fragments. However, there are problems when overwhelming psychological turmoil or conflict drives the individual to employ primitive defences in a rigid way. Rigid defences protect the ego but interfere with its capacity to perceive and respond to the demands of reality.

Example: Mrs. A. used to talk to her deceased husband of 35 years when she was on her own in the house. When asked about this habit, she said that she felt lonely, and talking to him made her feel less lonely.

By talking to herself, Mrs. A. denied the painful reality of her status as a widower in order to give herself some temporary relief from her loneliness and feelings of grief.

The super ego is the part of the mind that represents social norms and standards of behaviour and assesses us against these standards. Freud believed it was based on an identification with parental values. *A man finds a ten-pound note on the pavement outside a restaurant. He has a conversation with himself about whether to hand it in or not.*

This is a conversation in the man's mind between his *id*, "I could do with this money" and his super ego, "How would you feel if you lost a tenner and the person who found it just pocketed it?" The ego has to weigh up the conflict and make a decision about whether to hand over the money back, thus placating his super ego, or keep it, thus pleasing his id, but to find a way to live with the guilt generated by the super ego. A dilemma indeed!

Unconscious phantasy

Unconscious phantasy describes the mental activity lying behind conscious thought that structures the individual's relationships. The influence of the unconscious phantasy becomes evident when the individual is emotionally upset or disturbed.

Example: Ms. B. was an accomplished musician who suffered from performance anxiety, which inhibited her professional development. Although she knew logically that nothing terrible would happen if she made a mistake when performing, she struggled to overcome her anxieties. She was the older of two children, and when she was born her mother had suffered from post-natal depression. The patient also reported that her mother was critical of her and that she didn't ever feel she could satisfy her mother. At an unconscious level, the audience Ms. B. faced was her mother, who always looked at her critically.

Although Ms. B. realised that her anxiety was irrational, the fear of being a disappointment touched on deeper phantasies regarding her relationship with her mother.

Object

Object is the term psychoanalysts use to describe the internal representation of a significant person in the patient's life. When you find yourself talking to someone in your imagination you are talking to an internal object.

The transference and the counter-transference

Freud (1895) described transference phenomena in his early work with hysterics. He noticed the way patients unconsciously transferred repressed feelings and desires from childhood onto the therapist in the here and now. Initially, Freud thought that the transference was an obstacle to therapy; however, he later realised the transference could throw light on deep-seated, repressed childhood conflicts. Patients develop powerful, transferential feelings towards the professionals and carers responsible for their treatment. Professionals need to be sensitive to the meaning these roles carry for patients. It is important for them to try to tune in to patients' unconscious transference feelings towards them because this can convey meaningful insights into the nature of their early relationships and their underlying difficulties in relating to others.

Example: At short notice, I had to cancel the appointment of Ms. C., a 30-year-old woman who always felt she had been a disappointment to her parents. She was born after her mother miscarried a boy, and she believed her mother would have preferred the miscarried baby to be her. The patient arrived at the next session, saying that she nearly did not come as she had assumed the cancellation meant that I no longer wished to see her, and she believed that I would feel the therapy was a waste of my time. In her phantasy she thought I would have preferred to see a more satisfying, male patient.

Freud first described the term "counter-transference" to denote the patient's impact upon the therapist's unconscious mind (Freud, 1912). This idea was developed by Heimann (1950) to explain and make use of the therapist's feelings towards the patient. Her idea was that the patient-generated feelings in the therapist that were responses to the patient's own transference feelings, and if attended to, could prove illuminating about the patient's unconscious attitudes towards the therapist and the early attachment figures in their lives. Example: A patient started a session by making a provocative statement about my being a control freak and mean-spirited in my analysis of him. Feeling irritated, I replied by commenting on the patient's lack of gratitude for the help he had received. The patient triumphantly commented that this was exactly the sort of response he was talking about. Thus, I enacted the counter-transference by playing the role prescribed to me in the patient's transference (i.e. that I am mean and controlling). In hindsight, I realised it might have been better to point out the way the patient was trying to draw me into a familiar exchange in which he accused me and I would respond by accusing him in order to defend myself.

Money-Kyrle (1956) developed the theory of counter-transference by differentiating between normal and abnormal counter-transference. In normal counter-transference, the therapist takes in the patient's experience and subjectively identifies with them. The therapist then separates from the patient's subjective experience and objectively examines the interaction before deciding on an interpretation. In many ways, it is true to say that the therapist is having a conversation with themselves before talking to the patient. In the abnormal counter-transference scenario, the therapist may have difficulty separating their own self from identification with the patient and may react by treating the patient as if they were an aspect of their own self, rather than a separate Other. I believe this applies to all mental health work scenarios.

Example: This is often the dynamic behind heroic attempts at rescuing patients, a common dynamic with mental health professionals who break their code of ethics by developing inappropriate relationships with patients. Someone who is driven by the wish to protect patients from harm may find it difficult to leave the ward at the end of a shift or to switch off from work when they go home.

Klein worried that the development of the theory of counter-transference might lead to wild analyses as analysts could attribute ideas and feelings to the patient for neurotic reasons of their own. Hanna Segal (1981) wrote that counter-transference was the best of servants and the worst of masters. She too emphasised the need for the therapist to be cautious in attributing feelings in themselves to the patient. One of the functions of psychoanalytic supervision in mental health work is to provide the space to explore the mental health professional's emotional responses, to see how much light they shed on projective processes going on between them and the patient.

Example: Mr. D., a man in his late 30s, was plagued by a feeling that he was not working hard enough. He had been historically dogged by a feeling that his parents preferred his sister to him. He came into the session, sat down in the chair and after a few minutes of silence he said, "Your previous patient never shuts the outside gate and you do not ever seem to say anything to him about it." He then fell silent for a few minutes before saying, "Look I cannot afford to sit here wasting my time. If you have not got anything helpful to say I am going to leave." My immediate response was to feel guilty as if I had not been working hard enough or fast enough, leaving the poor patient suffering from anxiety about the threat of failure. After a pause, I began to find the space to separate myself from the effect of the patient's communication and to think that this must be what it was like to be him, constantly feeling that he was never doing enough and that he was being unfavourably compared to my other patients by a harshly judgemental me.

The paranoid-schizoid and depressive positions

Klein (1935) described the infant's dependence upon the mother for sustenance, care, and love in order to support the development of a strong mind and a healthy sense of self. When the infant feels safe, they feel in the presence of the "ideal" loving mother and have loving feelings towards her. The "ideal" mother is internalised by the infant and forms the basis of the infant's ego. However, when the infant feels anxious, in pain, or neglected, they feel they are in the presence of a "bad," threatening mother who fails to provide protection and care. Aggressive feelings towards this uncaring "bad" figure threaten the infant's developing ego and sense of security. In order to protect the ego and any residual good feelings about the ideal mother, the infant projects these aggressive feelings about the "bad" mother out into the external world. These aggressive feelings are then felt to reside outside the object in the external world and are always threatening to return. Klein described the way the infant internalises the good object it depends upon for life, in order to protect it, while projecting the bad, threatening object into an object in the external world (just think of how every fairy tale needs a "baddie"). The bad object is then attacked and treated as a threat, which needs to be kept outside, and Klein called this scenario the paranoid-schizoid position. The psychic defences used in the paranoid-schizoid position include splitting, projective identification, denial, and idealisation.

Example: Early in the morning on the way to work, I sat down on a train carriage opposite a man holding a can of strong lager and he looked drunk. I glanced at him in passing. He seemed to be waiting for me to look at him. He became aggressive, saying, "What the f*** are you looking at, you c***?"

In this instance, the man has split off and projected his conscience into me, so that he is able to enjoy his inebriated state, free of conflict and scrutiny. I then become his conscience looking at him in a moralistic and judgemental way, asking him questions like, "What are you doing drinking at this time in the morning while everyone else is going to work?" He then attacks me in a paranoid way, in order to get rid of the questions and the critical thoughts. So here we have the man splitting off part of his mind and then projecting this elsewhere, out of his mind. Hence, we call his state of mind "paranoid schizoid."

Over time, as ego strength develops, the infant begins to be able to lessen the split between their loved, "ideal" mother and the hated, "bad" mother. Indeed, the infant begins to realise their aggressive and loving feelings are directed towards the same person—their mother. The ideal object/mother is slowly relinquished and replaced by the "good enough" mother who can be ordinarily good at her job rather than having to be perfect. At the same time, the infant begins to realise they are dependent on this good enough mother for sustenance and life. The attacks upon the good enough object in phantasy cause feelings of guilt, sadness, and worry about the damage done. The infant begins to worry that their phantasised attacks will damage the same good enough mother the infant relies upon for care and sustenance. Anxiety about separation from this good enough object causes the infant to internalise the good object in order to protect her from aggressive attacks. The realisation of the good enough object's separate existence and vulnerability to attack and damage causes feelings of mourning as the infant is faced with their own and their object's vulnerability. Klein called this state of mind the "depressive position."

Example: In a psychotherapy session, a young woman, who persistently harmed herself, suddenly became aware of the fact that she had done tremendous damage to her body and her mind. She, bending forward in a way that conveyed her pain and sadness, said, "I can never repair the damage I have done to my body." She went on to say that she hoped she could stop self-harming because she still had a mind that had things to offer and she would like to get on with her work.

In this instance, we can see how the young woman becomes aware of the irreparable damage she has done to herself, and this leads to sadness about the loss. At the same time, she is able to stay with the sense of loss, resist the temptation to get back into further acting out, and express a wish to protect the functioning part of her that is not damaged.

Manic defences against persecution and guilt

Klein (1935) recognised that guilt and depression can lead to a regression into a manic state of mind, in which the infant tries to deny their dependence upon the object by denigrating the object and employing mechanisms of omnipotence to triumph over their dependency.

Example: Ms. E. was a 25-year-old woman with manic-depressive psychosis and a previous history of psychiatric admissions. She was being seen in once-weekly psychotherapy. She had been stable for a number of years and was due to get married to the supportive man she had been living with. Casual affairs with men had precipitated her breakdowns in the past. The patient reported that these men had several characteristics in common; notably, they were violent and good-looking. Historically, these affairs were often the precursors to manic breakdowns, in which she would damage the relationships she relied upon for support. Several weeks before an upcoming break in the therapy, Ms. E. told the therapist that she was sexually frustrated with her fiancé and had become attracted to a man who said he had been a member of a local gang and talked about killing men, which she found exciting. As the therapy break drew closer, she said that she was increasingly phantasising about the violent man and planned to see him the following week. She complained that her fiancé did not want sex as much as she did.

I think Ms. E. worried that her therapist was one of these weak men who found her demands too much and needed a break. The break would expose her to feelings of vulnerability and need which threatened to undermine her excited state of manic independence. In phantasy she turned to these powerful, macho figures who would help her triumph over vulnerability, anxiety, sadness, and loss.

Reparation and manic reparation

Klein (1929) described reparation as the impulse to repair the attacks on the object undertaken in unconscious phantasy. Klein believed that reparation was central to all creativity, as the individual wants to make amends for its attacks on the object through a creative act. Some reparative acts may take place in concrete external reality, while others are related to internal changes. As the creative act symbolically repairs the object, the ego is strengthened.

Example: Ms. F., a 28-year-old woman with a long-standing grievance towards her single mother for being overbearing, came into therapy complaining that she could not establish a life of her own as she felt this would damage her mother. After some time in psychotherapy, she began to develop a capacity to put herself first and bear the guilt involved in developing a life of her own. Just before a Christmas break, she told me she felt guilty, as she had told her mother that she had decided to go to her new boyfriend's parents for Christmas rather than spending it with her. She said that she felt her mother was hurt, but she was determined to put her own wishes first and bear the feeling of guilt. A few months later she told me that she and her boyfriend had decided to move in with one another, and she went through a similar feeling of guilt. She went on to say that she had just started playing the violin again, having not played since the age of 14. She started to cry as she remembered the pleasure both she and her mother got from her playing the violin as a child. Her mother had encouraged her to play the violin when she was younger, but she had given it up in her teens in a rebellious tantrum.

We can see in this example the way psychotherapy helps the patient separate from her mother and bear the guilt of putting herself first. This allows the patient to give up her stance of masochistic but resentful compliance. She is subsequently able to rediscover a pastime that gave them both pleasure when she was younger. In this way, she is able to bear the guilt of separating from her mother while rediscovering a warm and passionate relationship between herself and her mother, represented by the violin playing.

In contrast with reparation, which involves the experience of guilt, manic reparation employs omnipotent and manic defences in an attempt to repair the damaged object. The attitude towards the object often involves control and triumph rather than genuine remorse.

Example: A patient in the early stage of the therapy had a habit of going into loud and violent verbal outbursts when she was upset. As we came to the end of the therapy, she worried that she had damaged me through her verbal attacks and that I would be very keen to see the back of her.

Several weeks before the end of the therapy she told me of a dream. In the dream, I was speaking at a prestigious conference and she was in the audience with a friend. At the conclusion of my paper, there was a long ovation and the patient remembered feeling superior to her friend. I said I thought she wanted to end her treatment with a long applause, admiring me as a figure of eminence, as this allowed her to feel that she had received a superior therapy from a superior therapist. However, she worried that she could not protect anything ordinary from her criticism and contempt. She then said she remembered at the end of her dream seeing a beggar on the steps of the university. He was dishevelled, unkempt, and bald, and he reminded her of me!

In the example above, we can see the way the patient wishes to deal with her anxieties about the damage she may have done to me during the therapy by flattering me. However, the dream also reveals her triumphant feelings in relation to her friend. In this way, she tries to triumph over ordinary feelings of anger, disappointment, as well as gratitude about the end of the therapy. The association to the beggar on the steps of the university reveals the underlying anxieties about the damage she fears she may have caused me by her verbal attacks.

Projective identification

Klein (1946) used the term "projective identification" to describe an unconscious process by which a person gets rid of unwanted psychological knowledge or perceptions, while putting pressure on objects to conform to his or her omnipotent view of the world. This mechanism was key to the way the infant's functioning fluctuated between the disintegrated state of mind of the "paranoid schizoid position" and the integrated state of mind she called the "depressive position" (see above). In the paranoid-schizoid position, the infant's loving feelings for the mother are kept separate from its hateful feelings. Thus, the ego and the object are split between an idealised, loved object and a denigrated, hated object. Under the sway of the paranoid-schizoid position, the infant acts towards the external object as if *was* the element projected from the infant's mind.

Example: A patient I saw in psychotherapy had very little tolerance of his emotional difficulties and usually wanted to get away from the problem once he had told me the facts. Indeed, when I tried to think with him about the difficulty he had raised, he frequently said that he was bored with the subject and wanted to move on. The patient started one session by telling me about an upsetting argument that had occurred with his girlfriend over the weekend. I paused for a minute, thinking about his communication, and within a few seconds he asked me if I was bored. In a split second, the intolerance of his difficulties had been projected into me, and in *his* mind, *I* had become the one who could not stay with an emotionally upsetting problem.

The container and the contained

Bion (1962) described the infant's dependence upon the mother for emotional and psychological development as well as physical development. He outlined the way the infant's immature ego is overwhelmed and unable to process raw psychic experiences. Bion described the way the infant evacuates and communicates these raw experiences through noises, looks, and bodily movements. The mother takes in these raw experiences, before using her capacity to empathise and think about the infant's state of mind. Bion described this as the mother's capacity for reverie. In order for this process to work, the mother needs to be able to be affected by the infant's communication without being overwhelmed by it. The mother conveys her understanding of the communication through her actions and loving attitude. Thus, the mother's ability to "contain" the infant's raw emotions helps convert them into food for thought, which the infant can now internalise and digest. This gives the infant the feeling that they are being cared for by a figure that understands their feelings.

Example: A psychotic young man was shouting and screaming at a group of staff in the corridor of a large psychiatric hospital. The patient was agitated and threatening. The initial group of staff talking to the man were kind and calm but tried to get him to do things, "Why don't you come in here?" or "Why don't you take this to calm yourself down?" These reasonable requests led to the man becoming more agitated and defiant: "Why don't you all leave me alone; I'm going to break you all!" In addition to calling the emergency team, the ward manager had also called a well-known nursing assistant called Roberts. Roberts was an extremely large man who rarely felt threatened in physically threatening situations, and he had a reputation for calming down even the most psychotic and agitated patients.

When Roberts arrived, he walked purposely towards the patient and started talking to him in a calm but confident manner. He acknowledged the fact that the patient was upset about something and invited him to stay where he was and tell him what was bothering him. Roberts's calm concern was evident in his attitude and his voice. As this went on, the patient seemed to change from an agitated, aggressive and psychotic man to a much smaller, frightened, and distressed child. The whole atmosphere changed and the crisis began to dissipate.

Roberts's experience in dealing with these situations and his physical size meant that he was able to take in the patient's disturbance without feeling overwhelmed with anxiety about the physical threat (much as a much larger parent can do for the little baby). He was also able to realise that behind the threats and boastful claims of what the patient was going to do to the staff, the patient was in fact a frightened man. Thus, Roberts was able to contain the patient's extremely disturbed and threatening state of mind. This made the patient feel that he was with someone who was not terrified or alarmed by his communications but rather in the presence of someone able to both contain and understand him. The emergency team was not required.

Containment and the depressive position

The depressive position occurs when the infant is able to reduce the split between the good mother and the bad mother and begins to realise that the mother he hates is the same person as the mother he loves. This process of integration demands that the infant has internalised a good object capable of bearing painful emotions, as well as being able to reflect upon the meaning of those emotions.

The depressive position and the loss of the ideal mother coincide with the emergence of the Oedipal situation as the infant becomes aware of a third object, often the father. Knowledge of the parent's sexual relationship creates feelings of curiosity as well as jealousy and loss. The triangular relationship between the parents and the child closes a psychic space and provides boundaries around the child's experience of themselves. On the one hand, the infant has an experience of their mother taking in their subjective experience, while on the other hand, they are aware of a third object, the father, who is looking at the child's relationship with the mother from a different point of view. This model allows the integration of the infant's subjective experience of being understood emotionally by the mother with the objective experience of being thought about by the father from a separate point of view. This form of triangulation is necessary as it provides a space in which the other person can be thought about in their absence and paves the way for symbolic thought (Britton, 1989).

The Oedipal triangle and symbolic thinking

Freud (1897) coined the term "Oedipus complex" to describe the way the boy (3–5 years) harbours rivalrous feelings towards his father as he phantasises that he would like to murder his father while taking his father's place as his mother's partner. In the original myth, Oedipus unknowingly murders his father and marries his mother. Britton (1989) describes the importance of the Oedipal situation in supporting thought and the development of symbolic thinking. He emphasises the importance of the third object (psychically the father/partner) in supporting the mother-and-infant couple, while also providing room for separation and thought. The triangular situation provides a structure for thinking and helps prevent the collapse into concrete thinking or enactments.

Teams that treat patients whose clinical conditions are accompanied by disturbing psychological states of mind may need the help of an external supervisor. For example, patients in mental health settings with a diagnosis of borderline personality disorder often get under the skin of staff, while those with a diagnosis of anti-social personality disorder can induce sadistic responses from staff. These patient groups can have a profound impact upon staff capacity to think, which can undermine the team's capacity to contain their patients. By acting as the third point in the nurse-patient-supervisor triangle, the supervisor can provide an appropriate space for thinking about the psychological impact of the work on the staff member and thereby reduce the pull towards re-enactments (Evans & Franks, 1997).

Symbolisation and concrete thinking

Segal (1957) built on Klein's ideas by describing the difference between a symbolic representation and a symbolic equation. In the case of a symbolic representation there is an acknowledgement of the difference between the symbol and the object being symbolised. Thus, in saying, "I've got butterflies in my stomach" we are describing a sensation of things fluttering around in the stomach caused by anxiety or excitement. We don't actually mean we have butterflies in our stomach. However, in the case of a symbolic equation there is no differentiation between the symbol and the object. This gives rise to what we mean by concrete thinking—using words (symbols) as if they were the thing (object) itself. Patients in psychotic states of mind often think concretely and thus might hear someone saying, "I have butterflies in my stomach" as a statement of fact rather than a symbolic communication. In a symbolic equation state of mind, for instance, the statement "Give me a minute" is literally interpreted as 60 seconds rather than the symbolic meaning of the idea, which is, "Allow me some time." For example, on the ward, a psychotic patient may really struggle to stay calm after 60 seconds has elapsed if they have been waiting for a staff member. In order to maintain the difference between a symbolic equation and a symbolic representation, the subject needs to be supported in establishing a psychic separation from the concrete object. Britton (1989) described the third position as the place where some separation from the object could be achieved which provided room for reflection and symbolisation.

The psychotic and non-psychotic parts of the mind

Bion (1957) described the way a split can develop between a psychotic and a non-psychotic part of the mind. The psychotic part hates any knowledge of psychological pain, vulnerability, damage, or weakness, and tries to solve complex emotional problems through concrete physical actions. The psychotic part of the mind attacks the part of the mind that is capable of experiencing psychological pain and conflict. The ego's perceptual and thinking apparatus is attacked, fragmented, and projected into the external world. The person feels that the external world contains a fragmented element of their mind that threatens to re-enter the personality violently. Bion described these objects in the external world, which are believed to contain elements of their mind, as bizarre objects. Patients in a psychotic state of mind may project their capacity to see into an external object such as a clock, for example. Then they believe the clock, which now contains an element of their capacity to see, is looking at them. These external objects have a threatening and persecutory quality as they threaten to push themselves back into the patient's mind. The clock, which symbolises awareness and observation of the passage of time, threatens to force its way back into the mind of the patient who unconsciously wants to remain unaware of the way time passes. The vacuum left by the fragmentation and projection of parts of the patient's ego is then filled with an all-powerful and all-knowing delusional system. The delusional system is an attempt by the individual to repair a fragmented ego, in order to provide coherence and continuity. Propaganda emanating from the psychotic part of the personality is used to deny the reality of the damage it has done to the ego. The non-psychotic part of the mind is left with the difficulty of dealing with emotional problems while being undermined and attacked by the psychotic part of the personality. The psychotic and non-psychotic parts of the patient's mind are in a dynamic relationship and wrestle for control. Sometimes the psychotic patient will project the non-psychotic part of the ego, in order to free themselves from the pain of the conflict between the two parts of their mind.

Example: A ward manager from an acute psychiatric ward presented a patient who had taken his passport from the ward in order to withdraw some money from the post office. The previous week he had lost his bus pass and the ward manager was concerned he would also mislay his passport. On his return to the ward, she asked him where his passport was and, sure enough, he had lost it. She then asked the patient to remember his steps, in order to help find it, but the patient said he was too tired and could not be bothered.

The nurse became irritated, saying to the supervision group that she often found herself running around after this patient who tended to treat her as a servant. Mr. H. was a 40-year-old man, the eldest son of a successful academic. He had been a promising medic, before suffering from his first episode of mental illness at the age of 20. He had had placements in several mental health hostels, all of which had broken down on account of his superior and immature attitude towards community living and self-care. The ward manager said that this situation created a management problem because the patient was occupying a valuable in-patient bed and she was under pressure to discharge him, but he showed no inclination to rehabilitate himself or take any responsibility for his treatment.

During the supervision discussion, we thought about how the patient's actions seemed to symbolise something important about his mental state. He projected the non-psychotic part of his mind into the ward manager who had responsibility for looking after him. The ward manager acted like a mother who follows her child around, picking things up that have been used and discarded, once they have served their purpose. It would appear that until the patient was helped to develop an interest in his own identity, mind, and history, including the circumstances of his tragic and catastrophic breakdown, he would have difficulty taking any responsibility for the management of his illness.

The internal narcissistic gang

Rosenfeld (1971) developed the idea of a defensive structure that acted like an internal gang and offered protection from psychic pain, in return for loyalty. Any move by healthy aspects of the patient towards help may be undermined and attacked by the destructive aspects of their internal world. Although healthy elements of the patient may consciously wish to divorce themselves from the gang's influence, the person is often unconsciously dependent upon the gang in subtle ways. The healthy part of the patient needs help and support in its struggle with the internal gang and its attempt to form healthy relationships with good and helpful figures in the external world.

Example: Ms. I., a young woman with a long history of anorexia who had previously found it difficult to engage and make use of therapy sessions, started to engage and make emotional contact with the therapist. After three months where she appeared to be more available in the therapy and making progress, she retreated into a withdrawn, silent state of mind and started to lose weight. Eventually, after several sessions where the therapist attempted to take this up with her, she confessed that she heard a voice telling her not to talk to the therapist and not to eat.

The improvement in the patient's condition and her move towards life and dependency on the therapist provoked the gang to re-establish its control over the patient, by pulling her back into an anorexic state of starvation and self-suffiency. Separation from the influence of the gang often leads to an adverse therapeutic reaction.

Steiner (1993) built on Rosenfeld's work by describing the development of a "psychic retreat" within the patient's mind that acted as a resting place from anxieties associated with fragmentation, on the one hand, and development, on the other. He also emphasised the need for the clinician to respect the fact that patients will inevitably move in and out of their psychic retreats many times during the long, painful process of recovery and development.

Conclusion

In this second chapter, I have emphasised the relevance of psychoanalytic theory in helping to explain and understand clinical situations in mental health settings.

It is important to point out that we all rely on defence mechanisms and defensive psychic structures to protect the ego from being overwhelmed. However, there is a difference between psychotic and neurotic defences. Psychotic defences are based on splitting, projective identification, denial, and rationalisation.

Psychotic defences involve a gross distortion of psychic reality, which interferes with the individual's capacity to test and respond to the demands of internal or external reality. In the case of more neurotic defences such as displacement, reaction formation, isolation, undoing, and repression, there is only a partial distortion of reality. All of us revert to psychotic psychic defences from time to time when we feel overwhelmed. However, the fragility of the ego and/or severity of the super ego can mean some individuals find the frustration and anxiety involved in contact with internal and external reality difficult to bear. These individuals may become reliant on psychotic defences to protect their fragile ego from being overwhelmed.

It is also important to acknowledge that these psychic defences can occur within groups and institutions. Indeed, increased pressure on groups and individuals may push them towards psychotic forms of defence in an attempt to deny reality. In order to develop and maintain a balanced approach, clinical staff need settings and structures that help them digest the anxieties and pain involved in their work. Good enough support can be provided through clinical discussion, reflective practice, and good management. Bion (1962) developed the term "reverie" to describe the mother's capacity to respond imaginatively to the infant's communications. These reflective, organisational structures support the staff member through a process of containment, followed by separation and thought. Thus, reflective practice helps staff maintain the difference between the patient as a symbolic representation of internal figures in the mental health practitioner's mind and a concrete symbolic equation with them.

The theories outlined above are by no means a comprehensive list, but these are the main concepts I use throughout this book.

References

Bion, W. R. (1957). Differentiation of the psychotic from the non-psychotic personalities. *International Journal of Psychoanalysis*, *38*(3–4), pp. 266–275.

Bion, W. R. (1962). *Learning from experience*. London: Karnac Books.

Britton, R. (1989). The missing link: Parental sexuality and the Oedipus complex. In J. Steiner (Ed.), *The Oedipus complex today: Clinical implications* (pp. 83–101). London: Karnac Books.

Evans, M., & Franks, V. (1997). Psychodynamic thinking as an aid to clear thinking. *Nursing Times*, *93*(10), 50–52.

Freud, S. (1895). The psychotherapy of hysteria. In *The standard edition of the complete psychological works of Sigmund Freud*, Volume 11. London: Hogarth Press.

Freud, S. (1897). Letter 71. Extracts from the Fliess papers. In *The standard edition of the complete psychological works of Sigmund Freud*, Volume 11 (pp. 163–175). London: Hogarth Press.

Freud, S. (1912). The future of psychoanalytic therapy. In *The standard edition of the complete psychological works of Sigmund Freud*, Volume 11 (pp. 144–145). London: Hogarth Press.

Freud, S. (1923). The ego and the id. In *The standard edition of the complete psychological works of Sigmund Freud*, Volume 19 (pp. 3–66). London: Hogarth Press.

Heimann, P. (1950). On counter–transference. *International Journal of Psychoanalysis*, *31*, 81–84.

Klein, M. (1929). Infantile anxiety situations reflected in a work of art and in the creative impulse. In *The writings of Melanie Klein*, Volume 1 (pp. 210–218). London: Hogarth Press.

Klein, M. (1935). A contribution to the psychogenesis of manic-depressive states. *International Journal of Psychoanalysis*, *16*, 145–174.

Klein, M. (1946). Notes on some schizoid mechanisms. *International Journal of Psychoanalysis*, *27*(3–4), 99–110.

Money-Kyrle, R. (1956). Normal counter transference and some of its deviations. *International Journal of Psychoanalysis*, *37*(4–5), 360–366

Rosenfeld, H. (1971). A clinical approach to the psychoanalytic theory of the life and the death instincts: An investigation of the aggressive aspects of narcissism. *International Journal of Psychoanalysis*, *52*(2), 169–178.

Segal, H. (1957). Notes on symbol formation. *International Journal of Psychoanalysis*, *38*, 391–397.

Segal, H. (1977). Countertransference. *International Journal of Psychoanalytic Psychotherapy*, *6*, 31–37. Republished in *The work of Hanna Segal*. New York, NY: Jason Aronson. (1981), pp. 81–87.

Steiner, J. (1993). *Psychic retreats: Pathological organisations of the personality in psychotic neurotic, and borderline patients*. London: Routledge.

Chapter 3

Supervision and consultation

Tuning in to psychotic communications in front-line mental health settings

Patients who suffer from a serious and enduring mental illness often need psychological, chemical, and sometimes physical containment. The types of setting that provide this containment and the balance of the interventions used will vary according to the patient and his or her level of disturbance at any given time. However, the diagnoses and active interventions employed by psychiatry must be accompanied by a receptive approach to treatment and care. I believe mental health professionals need to take an interest in the meaning of their patients' symptoms and their verbal and physical communications, as they may convey important information about the patient's internal world and underlying conflicts. However, good mental health care—and treatment—also needs to go beyond this important first step by trying to understand the relationship between patients' presentations and their personalities. Indeed, highly disturbed patients need to be cared for by mental health professionals who are interested in and committed to understanding the meaning behind the presenting problem. This is because recovery will depend upon the patient's ability to reclaim his or her capacity for psychological thought and insight.

However, the development of insight itself can be a persecutory process, as patients become aware of the fragmentation of their minds and their detachment from shared reality. Depressed feelings commonly accompany insight as part of the process of recovering from a serious and enduring mental illness and patients often feel they are unable to face the full extent of their psychological difficulties. They may also worry that they are unlovable, unbearable, untreatable, and/or damaging to others. In desperation then, they may seek ideal or magical solutions to their problems—solutions that can impede the recovery process as patients may have developed a psychic structure designed to avoid painful realities. John Steiner (1993) makes the point that these defensive organisations need to be respected and understood, as they provide respite from demanding anxieties that have to do with fragmentation, on the one hand, and unbearable feelings of depression, on the other. Consequently, it is the mental health professional who, in the first instance, has to both develop and contain the insights into the nature of a patient's difficulties. Understanding the use of defences helps professionals to make sense of the patient's psychic structure.

In addition to experiencing feelings of anxiety, loss, and despair, patients who become aware of the extent of their difficulties are also prone to feelings of humiliation. Indeed, the dependence upon professionals and the inevitable imbalance between themselves and the perceived authority can highlight patients' feelings of inferiority. The fact that mental health professionals are required to assess the patient's state of mind can also exacerbate feelings of being looked down on, judged, or shamed. Professionals need to be sensitive to these feelings and, whenever possible, support patients in managing them. If professionals act in ways that are insensitive to patients' shame and humiliation, this may exacerbate historical feelings of resentment and unfairness in relation to authority figures. If these issues are not understood, they can become the locus of a grievance between patient and professional; this undermines the therapeutic relationship that is central to the process of recovery. However, even if professionals are sensitive to these issues, the sheer imbalance of power in the relationship can still inflame these dynamics. This becomes most evident when professionals are required to execute their professional roles and responsibilities.

In order to avoid the dynamics outlined above, professionals may find themselves adopting approaches that are affected by unconscious forces, as they attempt to avoid any stance that differentiates them from the patient. This loss of differentiation and reluctance to take up a position of professional authority can lead to the erosion of professional practice. An example of this can be seen when mental health clinicians reassure patients that their thinking is quite normal or "nothing to worry about" even when patients say they are becoming unwell. This reassurance leaves responsibility for the problem wholly with the part of the patient that is in touch with the extent of the difficulty. Numerous serious, untoward incident investigations have highlighted service failures to listen to patients who had reported that they were feeling unwell and in danger of harming themselves and others. Relatives have also often been ignored when they have recognised early signs of breakdown in the patient.

Effective mental health work depends on professionals' willingness to allow themselves to be disturbed by patients while still maintaining a professionally balanced view. However, establishing a therapeutic relationship with patients is complex and may itself be prone to false alliances, deceptions, and denial. These illusions and denials sometimes emanate from the patient, sometimes from the mental health professional, and sometimes from within the mental health system itself.

Psychoanalytic treatment is not widely available in the NHS. Although many patients with a severe and enduring mental illness or personality disorder may benefit from such treatment, it would not be the treatment of choice for all patients. Nevertheless, I would argue that an interest in the meaning of symptoms and behaviours should be seen as a cornerstone of *all* mental health treatment and care. Whether or not patients themselves are interested in the meaning of their symptoms, they do benefit from being treated by professionals who understand their point of view. Psychoanalytic thinking and insight provide a model for taking account of the unconscious forces that operate within therapeutic relationships and thus for understanding the meaning of symptoms. Clinical discussion about the nature of the relationship between staff and patients, including enactments, can throw light on the clinical problems underlying the patient's presentation and ways of relating, as the following three vignettes, in which consultation was sought, make clear.

Case example 1: The differentiation between health and illness

A mental health volunteer presented the case of Mr. J., who had a history of homelessness. He described the man as a lost soul, without personality or identity.

"I go around to see him every week. He is completely isolated, rarely speaks and spends his days staring at the wall. I think he is hearing or seeing things, as occasionally he responds to things going on in his mind by muttering or laughing to himself. The patient does not wash and the flat is filthy. I have tried to get him assessed by various different services because I think he is ill, but everyone says there is nothing wrong with him. When they ask him about psychotic symptoms, he denies them, saying only that he has dreams in front of his eyes. On one occasion, out of desperation, I took a mental health professional around to Mr. J.'s flat, so that she would see the state of his home, but he would not open the door. The professional said that the patient did not have to let her in, as this was his choice, and the visit was abandoned."

We can see here how Mr. J. denies the nature of his psychotic illness by keeping it to himself. He normalises his hallucinations by calling them "dreams in front of my eyes." The negative effects of schizophrenia have led him to withdraw from contact with the external world into a delusional world of his own creation. The patient's denial and rationalisation of his illness, combined with the pressure on the mental health professional to restrict the numbers on a caseload, can lead to a collusion between the mental health services and the patient where a delusion of sanity prevails.

Patients with serious and enduring mental illness need services and professionals who are able to listen, take in, and bear the pain of their psychological disturbance. However, the challenge for such professionals is to work out which part of the patient is talking, and with what aim. Is it the healthy part, in touch with psychic reality and the need for help? Is it the psychotic part, employing denial and rationalisation to conceal the real goal of manic self-sufficiency? Is it the perverse part, interfering with the establishment of a truthful picture? Or is it an infantile part that wishes to maintain a position of complete dependence? Healthy aspects of the mind that contain awareness and insight can find themselves wrestling with pathological or defensive elements of the mind, in an ongoing dynamic struggle.

The distinction between illness and health is useful when determining whether the patient's disturbance has moved from something that convention would describe as "within the normal range" to something that would be deemed "abnormal." This helps psychiatrists to make decisions about the necessity for treatment, the degree of their responsibility for the patient, and also whether the severity of the condition warrants compulsory detention of the patient in order to care for them safely. The distinction between illness and health provides the clarity necessary for making decisions about appropriate action.

As necessary as it is, however, this sort of medical categorisation does not provide a model for thinking about the dynamic interplay between different parts of the personality operating within and influencing the patient's mind. In the example described above, the mental health professional listens to Mr. J.'s denial and rationalisation of his illness and decides that he is well enough to make his own decisions. This leaves the patient untreated and the less experienced volunteer with responsibility for a man who is out of touch with the level of his disturbance. Thus, the professional and the patient alike have avoided painful thinking about the patient and the patient's state of mind.

Case example 2: Denial and rationalisation

A community psychiatric nurse (CPN) told a supervision group about a patient in a violent psychotic state, who had recently been admitted to the locked ward for the fourth time in as many years. Mr. K. had been discharged from the hospital six months earlier. He felt stigmatised by his psychiatric label and did not like the side effects of his medication. Within five weeks he had persuaded the CPN to discharge him from the follow-up, and soon after this, he stopped taking his medication. A few months later, he was detained under mental health legislation and admitted back to the locked psychiatric ward, due to his violent behaviour. The nurse explained that she had not liked being left with the feeling that her contact with the patient reminded him of his illness. The patient also felt that ongoing contact with psychiatric services undermined his self-esteem and his view of himself as better and stronger. Discharging the patient had also opened up a space in the CPN's overcrowded caseload.

I would argue the origins of the patient's breakdown can be traced back to the moment when the patient persuaded the CPN that he was well enough to stop having psychiatric follow-up and then discontinued his medication. The psychosis had by then already started to re-establish its hold within the patient's personality, as evidenced by his denial of any knowledge of his history, illness, or dependence upon the services, or of the likely outcome of these developments and actions.

Professionals have to listen to patients and consider their views, but the latter can express unrealistic demands, based on a wish to deny painful realities. Rather than just listening to these wishes and attempting to understand the patient's conflict and painful psychological state, the mental health system sometimes colludes by responding concretely. The capacity to depend upon others, which includes an awareness of limitations, is an important part of any patient's treatment, care, and potential for recovery. When patients reject the opportunity to form a helpful dependence, they may be forced back into the grip of more psychotic parts of their personality. This can increase risk and the danger of relapse as their underlying pathology goes unrecognised. The patient's wish to return to a self-sufficient state of mind that denies underlying difficulties to get away from the reality of their dependence may be understandable, as dependence makes them feel small, damaged, or humiliated. However, discharge from services may leave patients deprived of the appropriate psychiatric help when they find themselves at the mercy of their psychotic aspects.

When psychotic anxiety threatens to overwhelm the individual's ego, there is a collapse in the ego's capacity to manage the relationship between internal and external reality. Anxiety about the extent of the damage to their minds, both internally in phantasy and externally, can overwhelm patients with despair. This can drive them to resort to manic defences, based on magical thinking, in order to deny underlying feelings of guilt or impotence. Psychotic elements of the mind can promote unrealistic, omnipotent ideas of cure and self-sufficiency, while the parts of the self that acknowledge the need for healthy dependency are attacked and undermined. Patients in manic states often believe that they can deal with their underlying anxieties about damage by magical means. This includes putting psychic or physical distance between themselves and the problem, as if difficulties could be located in a particular geographical area and then left behind. In practical terms, this can lead to absconding, planning an unrealistic journey, or an unplanned change of job or partner. The problem with these mechanisms is that eventually when the defence can no longer be maintained, the patient breaks down.

In an attempt to regain control of this chaotic situation, some individuals may take drastic physical and psychological action: patients may, for example, act out violently in order to expel the overwhelming internal state, thereby forcing others to take control of their lives. Others whose minds fragment into psychotic states develop delusional systems which attempt to provide a rigid structure around a fragmented mind. The delusional system binds the fragmented parts of the mind together into a "coherent" belief system created by the patient. However, this belief system is based on a psychic structure that bears no apparent relation to external reality.

Case example 3: The psychotic and non-psychotic parts of the self

A social worker from a mental health team presented the case of Ms. L. who suffered from anorexia and had locked herself in her flat in order to starve herself. She had a habit of hoarding rubbish until it became a health hazard and posed a threat to other residents, whereupon environmental health officers had to be alerted. The patient telephoned the social worker and said that she felt suicidal and wanted to die. The social worker visited the patient at home, but she refused to open the door, so she had to conduct a constrained and restrained interview with the patient through the letterbox. She said that she was worried about the patient and was going to talk to her GP to arrange a domiciliary visit.

However, Ms. L. threatened to take legal action against the social worker if she contacted the GP. A solicitor then telephoned the social worker to complain about her attempt to speak to the patient through the letterbox, saying that she "would take out a charge of harassment" against the social worker who was "interfering with the patient's human rights." Several days later she received a letter from the patient's solicitor confirming this threat and warning that she should not be in touch with the GP under any circumstances. The social worker felt utterly helpless and that she was losing her mind as, on the one hand, she had a duty of care to an ill patient, while, on the other, she was herself in danger of litigation and prosecution if she took what she considered to be appropriate action.

Bion (1957) described a division in the patient's mind between the psychotic and the non-psychotic (or sane) part. The psychotic part of the mind hates all emotional contact, psychic pain, and meaningful emotional ties. This part of the mind uses violent projection in order to get rid of any awareness of painful conflicts or emotions. The non-psychotic part has the job of thinking about conflicts to do with emotional pain and meaning. The patient's mind may oscillate in functioning between these two states, in what Bion described as "the conflict, never decided . . . between the life and death instincts" (1957, p. 44). When the psychotic part of the mind is in the ascendency, it may fragment and project the non-psychotic part in order to undermine its capacity to bear the demands of reality. The vacuum left in the ego is then filled with magical or wishful thinking.

In the case of Ms. L., we can see how the sane part of the mind is being held hostage by the psychotic part. Although the sane part of the patient made fleeting, limited contact with the social worker through the initial phone call telling her she was feeling suicidal, the psychotic, murderous part then stepped in and attacked the contact. This was done by threatening the social worker with accusations of professional misconduct if she went against Ms. L.'s wishes. The solicitor had also been coerced by propaganda emanating from the psychotic part of the patient, designed to undermine the social worker's role and authority. Of course, the patient's sane awareness still relied upon the social workers' resilience and capacity to hold on to the bigger clinical picture and, indeed, the social worker's gut reaction was to realise that the threats were part of the patient's illness and that the psychotic part had taken the sane part of her patient's personality hostage.

But Ms. L.'s behaviour left the social worker feeling trapped on the horns of a dilemma: if she did nothing, her patient's condition would deteriorate further; if she acted, she could be prosecuted for abusing Ms. L.'s human rights. This feeling of being trapped gave the social worker the experience of what it must be like to be in Ms. L.'s shoes, when the sane part of her mind drew attention to the extent of her illness but is then undermined by the attacks of the psychotic part. We can see how Ms. L.'s mental state fluctuated as the dynamics of her internal world changed. At one point, the non-psychotic part of her mind became aware that she was trapped inside a murderous psychotic state that wanted to starve her to death. This sane part of her mind was then able to let the nurse know that she was afraid of being caught in its grip. Once she had made the social worker aware of her precarious state, Ms. L. promptly withdrew into the psychotic part of her mind, denying there was a problem and then attacking and undermining the social worker's appropriate concern.

In the discussion, the nurse said that she had felt intimidated by Ms. L.'s threat of legal action, but she knew she could not leave the patient on her own. The social worker said that she found the discussion helpful, as it enabled her to think clinically about the situation. She also realised she needed the consultant psychiatrist's support in standing up to the intimidation from the psychotic part of the patient. The social worker subsequently reported to the supervision group that she had conducted a domiciliary visit with the consultant, who told the patient that unless she complied with psychiatric care, he would be forced to request a Mental Health Act assessment. The patient agreed to comply and the need to section the patient was avoided.

In this case, consultation and supervision provided timely support for the social worker in her difficult work with Ms. L. by enabling a space for thinking about the underlying psychotic process. Together, we were able to consider the meaning of this anxiety-provoking and frustrating situation. Once we could think of the fluctuations between the psychotic and the non-psychotic parts of the patient's personality, it was possible to understand her perplexing presentation. The supervision group was able to help the social worker separate from the tyrannical influence of Ms. L.'s psychosis by helping her understand the way she had been split off from her relationship with the psychiatrist in her mind. The restored relationship between social worker and psychiatrist formed an authoritative clinical structure that could now better withstand the threats and projections emanating from the psychotic part of the patient's mind. (We also discussed that the solicitor would need some help to free herself from the influence of the patient's psychotic propaganda.)

Case example 4: The psychotic patient's murderous attack on sanity

Mental health staff from both in-patient and out-patient services presented the case of Mr. M., a patient who had been treated by the mental health trust for many years. He had a treatment-resistant condition which involved him believing he was the Prophet Muhammed. Post-discharge he would preach in the street, and then take food from supermarkets. When apprehended by security in the store, he would assault staff saying that he was the Prophet Muhammed and didn't have to pay. On admission, staff reported he would take medication and comply with ward routines provided they refer to him as "the Prophet" and that he assaulted them if they called him by his given name. The group broke out into an argument as some members of the group said calling him "the Prophet" colluded with his delusional beliefs, while others said it went against their religious beliefs to call him "the Prophet."

The group then started to discuss whether he was on the correct anti-psychotic medication, although it was clear the treatment-resistant nature of his condition meant he had probably tried every form of anti-psychotic medication available. I interrupted the discussion to ask the staff to tell us something about Mr. M.'s history, personality, and life. What was striking was that although he was well known throughout the mental health trust because of his difficult behaviour, very little was actually known about him. Eventually, one nurse who had known him for many years said that he had been brought up in care homes from an early age and managed to work in a professional job until breaking down in his late 20s. He had suffered a depressive breakdown at this time and never recovered. The group then went back to discussing how to treat the psychosis. I interrupted the discussion to point out that "the Prophet" and the preoccupation with the psychosis was not only dominating his life but also dominating our preoccupations. I made the point that while we, quite rightly, wanted to treat the patient's mania and grandiose delusion, he seemed equally determined to hold onto his psychosis. He seemed to have no intention of relinquishing his loud and notorious claims to be at the centre of one of the world's great religions in order to get back to being himself. Who can blame him? According to what we knew of his history, Mr. M. seemed to be a man who had got himself together despite his unpromising start in life by managing to train in a profession, before suffering his depressive breakdown, in which, one would imagine he had felt small, unloved, and unwanted. Thus, a mental health trust focuses on its goal of removing his psychosis, all the while revealing they are at odds with the patient who has no intention of allowing us to make him depressed again by giving up his right to be "the Prophet."

Attempts to eradicate the psychosis

At times, patients try to eradicate their psychosis through acts of suicide—"I'll kill it off." Alternatively, they try to exclude all emotions and move into a state of mind dominated by schizoid logic. Although psychotic states of mind are serious and may cause considerable suffering and pain to patients and their relatives, the psychosis cannot be eradicated, as it represents an aspect of the patient's mind. This is not to say that psychosis and its side effects should not be treated medically; the danger is, rather, that we may further persecute patients if we give the impression that we find aspects of their minds intolerable. The psychotic part of the personality may be a destructive aspect, but it cannot be eradicated and needs to be thought about and accounted for. Indeed, the psychotic part of the personality is likely to feel threatened by therapeutic work which claims to want it eradicated. Mental health care professionals need to be sensitive to the fact that the psychotic part of the personality may feel excluded and unwanted, instead it is more effective to try to "tune in to the psychotic wavelength" (Lucas, 2009) in order to support their patients' struggle with the psychotic aspects of themselves.

Even patients diagnosed as suffering from a neurotic condition or personality disorder, who may not be obviously out of touch with reality, can demonstrate evidence of what psychotherapists may describe as psychotic thinking. Though not necessarily psychotic from a psychiatric point of view, these manifestations may nevertheless be based on omniscient and omnipotent ways of thinking that are encapsulated within a neurotic symptom.

Acutely disturbed individuals require mental health services to take action and intervene actively in their lives, even sometimes against their will. This is an important function of psychiatry and psychiatric practice and a reluctance to act may be destructive and unhelpful. However, mental health services also need to take in and think about the meaning of their patients' symptoms, behaviours, and actions. As I have argued throughout this chapter, it is the absence of an adequate model for thinking about the effects of psychotic communication that can leave professionals in danger of reacting to unconscious forces without understanding them.

Discussion

Investigation of the patient's mind is an important part of good mental health practice, and mental health professionals need the authority and skill to carry this out in a humane way. The nature of psychosis is such that destructive aspects of the personality, which hate any acknowledgement of need, may attack and undermine either the patient's sanity or the mental health professionals' attempts to help.

From time to time, of course, the non-psychotic part of patients' minds may be completely overwhelmed by psychosis in a way that forces them to act out their destructiveness physically, resulting in a threat either to themselves or to others. When this happens, the patient may need to be physically contained (under the Mental Health Act 1983) and treated with medication. These interventions are not a substitute for psychological care, but they may be necessary in order to safely care for the patient (Alanen, 1997).

What all three of the above clinical examples suggest is that an important part of any patient's recovery is based on the capacity to mourn the loss of the ideal self and to face painful realities. This involves taking back aspects of the self that have been denied, split off, and projected. There are inevitably cycles in this recovery, as it moves between periods of development and mental integration and periods of disintegration and regression. This is a precarious process that may lead to feelings of guilt and despair, followed by fragmentation and a retreat into paranoia, which acts as a defence against depressive feelings about the damage that may have been perpetrated.

The mental health system has to contain and care for patients with profound psychological difficulties and fragile egos that are prone to fragmentation in the face of painful psychological anxieties and conflicts. Their minds may also be inhabited by destructive aspects of the personality that offer psychotic solutions to problems in order to avoid painful psychic realities, rather than experience and bear them. These various elements wrestle for control over the mind as the patient's functioning veers between psychotic and non-psychotic modes.

Patients who suffer from a psychotic illness and personality disorder may find it hard to face the extent of their difficulties and suffering. The patients may withdraw from the world of shared emotional meaning into a preoccupation with states of mind based on omnipotence and omniscience. Ordinary communication may be stripped of its symbolic value and the patient may lose the capacity to convey emotional significance, creating a gulf that leaves mental health professionals and relatives feeling alienated and deprived of meaningful contact with them.

The danger is that mental health professionals can respond to patients' attacks on making psychological meaning by becoming mechanistic in their thinking, leaving patients feeling that they are being dealt with by professionals who keep them and their suffering at too great a distance. Professionals may unconsciously go along with patients' denial and rationalisation by trying to understand them at a neurotic level and join them in a manic denial of serious problems. This may alleviate painful realities about the extent of the patient's damaged thinking, but the patient's sane part is then left to manage the psychotic part alone, without any psychological support. Alternatively, mental health professionals may try to crush the psychosis by attacking it with aggressive doses of medication designed to eradicate psychotic signs and symptoms. This is sometimes encouraged by the patient who would like to resolve the conflict between the psychotic and the non-psychotic part of the mind. They sometimes find a solution to this conflict by retreating into a delusional world of their own creation.

Conclusion

In recent years, funding for mental health services in the United Kingdom has been consistently cut more drastically than for acute medicine. These financial cuts have driven commissioners to push for reductions in staffing levels, restrict numbers of senior staff grades, close beds, and employ shorter treatment lengths. The shortage of resources can encourage the employment of manic defences in the mental health system. Treatment length is increasingly based on limited resources rather than on clinical evidence. In spite and in the face of these fiscal and political developments, I would still contend that each patient's state should, as far as possible, be seen and understood within the context of its overall development and history.

Mental health professionals need to try to take a long-term view of their patients, including the fact that they may move in and out of illness over long periods of time. Managers and commissioners need to be helped to understand that mental illness is damaging and serious and at times dangerous and unpredictable, so cannot usually be managed on a short-term, one-off basis. In an attempt to reduce costs, the squeeze on the time available for teaching, supervision, and case discussion undermines the reflective capacity of individuals and teams, thus weakening the structures that support the staff's capacity to digest clinical experience. There is a danger of creating, in the place of these structures, a system that increases the distance between suffering patients and mental health services and professionals.

In the light of these worrying developments, clinicians need to do their utmost to maintain the intimate connection and complementarity between the treatment of patients with severe and enduring personality disorders and the supervision of front-line staff. On the one hand, the experience of once- or twice-weekly work with ill patients in psychoanalytic psychotherapy gives clinicians first-hand experience of the emotional field involved in the treatment of such patients. The ongoing clinical struggle keeps therapists alert to the general difficulties of the work, and this, in turn, helps supervisors stay in touch with the limitations of understanding. On the other hand, supervising staff managing acutely ill patients can keep therapists in contact with severe psychopathology on the mental health front-line. Such mutuality is crucial.

The psychoanalytic model is particularly helpful when thinking about psychotic or borderline functioning and it can restore the missing emotional meaning to concrete communication or acting out. It can improve clinicians' capacity to remain interested in their patients' emotional life and enable clinicians to listen out for rare moments of meaning, even where the predominant or prevailing discourse seems utterly stripped of significance and dominated by "madness."

Patients who act out their disturbance in dramatic ways, who project into their bodies or develop sado-masochistic relationships with others, need mental health staff to be interested in understanding the nature of such communication. This does not necessarily mean that the patient either wants or could manage insight at this acute stage of the illness. However, most patients benefit from feeling that they have been understood, even if they become disturbed by the insights. Insight into the nature of patients' difficulties needs first to be understood and worked through by the clinicians themselves, before it can be interpreted to patients.

This is particularly important when treating patients who are not able to bear the psychological pain involved, until there is a feeling that they have secured the understanding and support of their therapists. Ill patients can have a considerable effect on staff, by provoking them into acting out and these enactments need to be processed by the staff before the underlying issues can be worked on in the therapeutic relationship.

Working with people who have mental illness can be rewarding and enlightening, but it can also be frightening, boring, frustrating, anxiety-provoking, and stupefying. Patients' communications and actions can have a disturbing effect on mental health professionals and can provoke them into reactions that try to control the patient's thinking or behaviour. Although at times actions taken by staff are appropriate and necessary, they may also be driven by a wish to curtail provocative or disturbing elements of the patient's mind.

Ultimately, it is incumbent upon both staff and patients to try to understand the disruptive and destructive elements in their own thinking. Without this deeper understanding, there will be missed opportunities, as the underlying meaning of communications are lost, ignored, or crushed.

Finally, in order for this receptive capacity to be sustained in the minds of staff, staff need to feel looked after and to know that senior clinical management take their concerns and feelings seriously. If they do not feel cared for, the morale of mental health professionals can be badly affected and staff become more anxious and less psychologically receptive to their patients. Ultimately, care for staff usually leads to better care for patients, a consequent reduction in serious, untoward incidents, and a reduction in staff sick leave rates.

References

Alanen, Y. O. (1997). *Schizophrenia; its origins and need-adapted treatment.* London: Karnac Books.

Bion, W. R. (1957). Differentiation of the psychotic from the non-psychotic personalities. *International Journal of Psychoanalysis, 38*(3–4), 266–275.

Lucas, R. (2009). Education in psychosis. In D. Birksted-Breen (Ed.), *The psychotic wavelength, A psychoanalytic perspective for psychiatry* (pp. 280–299). London: Routledge.

Steiner, J. (1993). Two types of pathological organizations. In *Psychic retreats: Pathological organisations of the personality in psychotic neurotic, and borderline patients.* (pp. 116–130). London: Routledge.

Chapter 4

Therapeutic and anti-therapeutic factors in therapeutic relationships

The NICE guidelines for patients who suffer from severe and enduring mental illness or personality disorder advocate the "therapeutic relationship" should be one of the main pillars of treatment. In this chapter, I am going to describe some of the therapeutic and anti-therapeutic factors inherent in therapeutic relationships, highlighting the therapist's ability to tune into the psychotic level of communications. Caring for a patient with psychotic experiences or beliefs puts enormous pressure on the professional. The professional is often placed in a position where he or she may either deny some aspect of the patient's state of mind or collude with the patient or act out by re-enacting some aspect of the patient's internal drama. It is crucial therefore that the professional is able to identify and locate these pressures; otherwise the therapeutic relationship can become destructive. This can lead to repetitive and sometimes destructive patterns of behaviour between the professional and the patient. Whilst psychiatry limits psychosis to a group of disorders where hallucinations or delusions are prominent, in psychoanalytic study—and increasingly in psychosis research—these processes are recognised to be present in people without psychotic disorders. It is also important to acknowledge that even patients who suffer from a non-psychotic disorder have psychotic areas of functioning in their mind that professionals need to identify and understand. These interactions are part of all therapeutic work, and not all enactments are avoidable. They can provide an opportunity to deepen our understanding of the underlying clinical situation as they throw light on deeper layers of the clinical situation.

The term "breakdown" describes the damage done to the ego when the individual is overwhelmed by anxiety or extreme emotion. The ego starts to fragment in the face of these psychic storms, and aspects of its functioning are disowned, projected, or impaired. Indeed, the ego's functions are often projected into the external world and affect the way the individual relates to others. The breakdown may be a transient state of mind or become part of a chronic psychological illness. A patient who suffers from a serious and enduring mental illness may be admitted to a mental health setting for treatment and care. To some extent, the professional's capacity to think about their patients has replaced the asylum as the "container" for fragmented aspects of the patient's mind.

Recovery depends upon the ability of the patient to regain aspects of his/her ego as a process of mental reintegration through insight. Gaining insight is the process by which the patient restores their ego functioning and their capacity to think about themselves in relations to others. The capacity for insight, otherwise known as "self-awareness," is dynamic and fluctuates according to the individual's capacity to bear painful knowledge about themselves in relation to others. No matter how seriously the individual seems to be dislocated from reality, there is always a healthy part of the self that is trying to restore the damaged ego. Psychic growth and health is dependent upon an accurate assessment of the relationship between internal and external reality. The therapeutic relationship can play a central role in the patient's recovery as it provides both emotional support and feedback that can lead to the development of insight.

However, establishing a therapeutic relationship with patients is complex and may itself be prone to false alliances, enactments, deceptions, and denial. The development of insight can itself, however, be a persecutory process as patients become aware of the fragmentation of their minds and their detachment from shared reality.

In the United Kingdom, many mental health professionals receive little training in therapeutic approaches to their work. There are mental health teams who remain thoughtful in the face of extreme pressures and individuals who are naturally gifted and able to relate to patients in an open way. However, this lack of training which might be able to provide a clinical model that helps clinicians make sense of unconscious dynamics, can leave professionals poorly equipped to deal with the underlying psychological pressures inherent in their work. For example, mental health professionals might be unaware of the patient's dependence upon them and the way their presence or absence may affect the patient's mental state. Dependence is often talked about in mental health settings as if it is a bad thing, rather than an essential ingredient in fostering development and recovery. When professionals fail to recognise their significance to a patient, it can leave patients feeling that professionals are out of touch with their emotional needs.

Effective therapeutic work depends on the willingness and ability of mental health professionals to be disturbed by the patient while maintaining a professionally balanced view. Unconscious communications can put pressure on the professionals to either act out or deny aspects of reality. I would describe these as enactments as the professional is provoked into reacting in response to unconscious communications. These interactions are part of all therapeutic work and are not avoidable. Indeed, they provide an opportunity to deepen our understanding of the underlying clinical situation as they throw light on deeper layers of the clinical situation.

In this chapter, I am going to describe some of the therapeutic and anti-therapeutic factors inherent in relationships, highlighting the importance of tuning into the unconscious levels of communication and especially the psychotic ones. I am also going to give examples of the way that a psychoanalytic approach can provide a model of the mind that allows for an understanding of both unconscious and conscious communications. This model can help mental health professionals make sense of the interpersonal dynamics that operate in their therapeutic relationships.

Psychotic defences

We all need defences against psychic pain, and some of these defences will include primitive areas of psychic functioning that involve violent splitting, projection, and denial of internal and external reality. These primitive states of mind often become more influential when we feel overwhelmed with anxiety about fragmentation, damage, or guilt. We are also susceptible to the appeal of primitive defences, especially when they promise magical, pain-free, ideal solutions. But these often turn out to be based on the psychotic mechanisms of omniscience and omnipotence. Such states of mind and their influence are often easier to recognise when the presentation is florid, but may be less easy to spot when concealed behind denial and rationalisation. The universal appeal of these psychotic mechanisms means that they can have a contagious effect upon professionals as they touch on deep-seated, unconscious desires within all of us for pain-free solutions.

Therapeutic relationships

When things are going well, the professional takes in and empathises with their patient's situation. In order to "identify" with the patient, we use our own experiences to place ourselves in their position. Problems arise when the professional becomes either overwhelmed or over-identified with the patient. When this happens, the professional's anxiety may then become abnormally high, leading to anti-therapeutic behaviour in the therapeutic relationship. For example, the professional may attempt to cure the patient through heroic efforts. This is one of the dynamics which drive acts of professional misconduct, as attempts to rescue the patient lead to breaches of professional boundaries. Alternatively, the professional may attempt to distance themselves from the patient, who is believed to contain damaged and damaging states of mind. When this happens, the professional may develop a hard, external skin designed to keep the patient and their disturbance at a distance and give the impression of cruel indifference.

To develop and maintain a balanced approach, clinical staff need settings and structures. Further, they need a model that helps them to digest the anxieties and pain involved in therapeutic relationships. Support needs to be provided through supervision, reflective practice, and clinical discussion. These opportunities can help some professionals separate from their identification with the patient and restore an objective clinical approach, while they help others reflect on their hardened attitudes, in the interests of becoming more emotionally available. This kind of clinical space for reflection can lead to a renewed interest in the emotional communications of their patients and prevent harmful enactments.

In the following clinical examples, I will outline some of the psychoanalytic concepts I find helpful when thinking about therapeutic relationships, including: transference, projective identification, the psychotic and non-psychotic parts of the personality, and counter-transference. Although three of the examples are taken from individual NHS psychotherapy, which is designed to focus on unconscious communication, these dynamics occur in all mental health settings and treatments. I have used the term "therapist" to describe the interactions that take place in the individual psychotherapy examples and the term "mental health professional" to describe all other professional activities.

Case example 1: Transference enactment

Freud (1912) coined the term "transference" to describe the way the patient re-enacted aspects of their history in relation to the professional. Klein (1935) emphasised the fact that these re-enactments also throw some light on infantile aspects of the patient's internal world. In the transference, the patient may act in ways which nudge the professional into certain behaviours which fit with the historical and current structure of the patient's internal relationships.

In this example, I am going to describe how I became caught in a transference re-enactment with a once-weekly psychotherapy patient, which led to an impasse in the therapeutic relationship.

Ms. N. was a singer who suffered from crippling performance anxiety. The origins of her anxiety lay in her childhood where she developed a deep-seated rivalry with her adopted younger sister. In effect, the patient believed she had a perfect relationship with her mother and the adoption of her sister shattered her illusion. She was preoccupied by a grievance towards her parents, whom she believed had ruined her life by adopting a child. The patient felt pushed out, unloved, and unwanted since the adoption of her sister. The patient frequently complained to me that the purpose of her therapy should be to cure her social anxiety and enable her to become a world-renowned singer, thus regaining her place as the apple of her mother's eye. Thus, rather than mourning the loss of her ideal state and accepting the reality of her adoptive sister's existence, the patient believed she could have the ideal state restored.

In contrast to this, I believed that the purpose of her therapy was to help the patient understand herself, which included awareness of her dependence upon manic states of mind which were employed to deny rather than face reality. Daydreams are an important part of psychic life as they indicate areas of wishful thinking and are freer from objective evaluation. For example, some daydreams inspire us to strive to achieve something in the external world, which in turn requires that we recognise the reality of the work that needs to be done in order to achieve our dreams. This includes acknowledgement of the difference between our daydreams and the work required to achieve our goals in external reality. Other daydreams are based on the wish to deny the demands of external reality by offering an internal phantasy solution.

Ms. N.'s central phantasy was that the therapy would help her become a person that could finally triumph over her sister as her mother's partner. However, when the analysis failed to provide her with this solution, she became extremely aggrieved. Any movement or interest in development in the therapy could provoke a negative therapeutic reaction as the patient believed her difficulties were being forgotten about or not properly recognised by me. On the contrary, she felt she must remind me of the extent of her difficulties and the analysis' failure in restoring her to an ideal state.

If I pointed out progress in the therapy that often got denied or devalued, Ms. N. accused me of being in a rush to see improvement and denying the unsolved problems. In the transference, I became like the mother who rushes off to adopt her sister leaving her feeling abandoned and uncared for.

Sometimes when I pointed things out as part of the therapy, she felt I was using the therapy to triumph over her like a rivalrous sister. Indeed, she sometimes believed I used the therapy in order to endorse my own feelings of superiority.

If I pointed out that Ms. N. had difficulty acknowledging the progress we had made together, she withdrew into a paranoid and aggrieved state of mind and our relationship reached an impasse. In this way, I enacted the transference by trying to force my view of events onto her, acting as if I thought she should submit to my superior knowledge of the situation. However, when I examined the interaction between myself and the patient after the session, I was able to reflect on the repetition of her early relationship with her sister in the transference and counter-transference. I was then able to interpret to her that I felt she saw me as the rival, whose work with her was being used to establish my superiority over her rather than to help her. This enabled me to deepen my understanding of her difficulties and continue with our therapeutic work. Thus, my capacity to recognise and understand (rather than enact the transference) helped us turn a therapeutic impasse into a therapeutic opportunity, by deepening our understanding of obstacles to the patient's progress.

Rather than helping them to face loss, many patients believe that therapy should help them return to a previously perceived position of invulnerability. However, this is a problematic expectation, as their pre-existing state of mind may have been built on what we call "magical thinking." This is thinking that is based on wishful thinking and bears no relationship with reality. The therapeutic relationship needs to be concerned with the issue of how to interpret the patient's devotion to an ideal solution to their difficulties, one which protects them from their underlying feelings of dependence or vulnerability.

When patients become aware of the extent of their difficulties, they have to face up to their feelings of anxiety, loss, despair, and they are also prone to feelings of humiliation. Dependence upon mental health professionals and the inevitable imbalance in power can highlight feelings of inferiority. The fact that professionals are required to develop an objective view of their patient's state of mind and functioning can also exacerbate feelings of being looked down on, judged, or shamed. Professionals need to be sensitive to these feelings and, whenever possible, help support patients in managing them. If professionals act in ways that are insensitive to these feelings of shame and humiliation, it can exacerbate feelings of resentment and unfairness in relation to authority figures from the patient's past. If the transference aspect of early infantile dependence on the parent is not appreciated, it can be re-enacted in a manner which undermines the therapeutic relationship central to the patient's recovery.

Over identification

To avoid the dynamics outlined above, professionals may find themselves adopting approaches that are affected by powerful unconscious forces, as they become trapped in an identification with the patient. This concrete identification amounts to a collapse in the therapy as the patient is deprived of a relationship with their professional as a separate person. The reality is that during the process of recovery, the patient may feel small and humiliated from time to time, as they become aware of their dependence upon others for help. When patients reject the opportunity to form a helpful dependence, they may be forced back into the grip of more psychotic parts of their personality. This can increase the risk and the danger of relapse, as their underlying pathology goes unrecognised. It is worth noting, however, that even if professionals are sensitive to these issues, the imbalance of power between patient and professional can still inflame these dynamics; this becomes most evident when professionals are required to take responsibility for the patient and their behaviour.

Case example 2: The effect of projective identification on the therapeutic relationship

Melanie Klein (1935) described the way patients project aspects of their internal world into what we call an "external object," which in the case of therapy is often the therapist. This projection is often accompanied by actions that are designed to produce a reaction that coheres with the patient's perception. In this way, a person who is convinced their partner is uncommitted pushes them away until they give up on the relationship, whereupon the person can say, "I told you weren't really committed." In the example below, I will describe the way I was affected by projective identification, which led to an enactment and a threatened breakdown in the therapeutic relationship with a patient in once-weekly psychotherapy.

Mr. O., a 45-year-old single father of a child with learning difficulties, was referred by a senior colleague who occupied the room next to mine. My colleague had warned me that the patient was prone to violent temper tantrums and had kicked a chair across the consulting room. Mr. O. complained that he was a single parent who was left to fight for himself and his daughter by an indifferent and self-satisfied system. He also felt that he was easily dismissed as unreasonable because from time to time he lost his temper and shouted. This tended to happen when he felt that either he or the other person had failed to live up to an ideal, and he felt humiliated.

Just before seeing him for the first time, I fell ill and had to cancel the session. On meeting him at the rearranged appointment, Mr. O. said this was the sort of rubbish treatment he was used to and that he wanted my colleague to treat him instead. He asked, "Why don't I ever get the help I need?" He looked around my room complaining about the decor and commented that he could not be seen by someone who took so little care over the things they were responsible for. I said that I thought he was angry at being transferred from someone he felt had listened to him and taken him seriously, to someone like me who cancelled appointments and made him feel that he was unimportant. He started to scream at the top of his voice and said that he was used to being let down, as that was the story of his life. I said that I thought he was shouting because he wanted his previous therapist next door to hear his loud complaints so they would know how let down and angry he felt. At this point, the patient stood up, screamed he was leaving, and left the room, violently slamming the door.

On reflection, I realised, that by mentioning his wish to let my colleague know that he was angry, I had responded in a way that made him feel small and blamed for complaining. I think his loud criticism, which I imagined my colleagues could hear, induced a feeling of shame in me—would my colleague think I was making a mess of her careful work with this patient? In this way, I became identified with the patient's difficulty of being measured against an ideal. In a knee-jerk response, I attempted to push the feeling of shame back into the patient, which led to a breakdown in our therapeutic relationship.

To my surprise, Mr. O. attended our second session. He said he had tried to phone the previous day to check that the session was on but that no one had got back to him. His words were, "You people don't communicate." He went on to say that he did not want to see me, as he did not feel that I took his difficulties seriously and that I was a "jobsworth." He said that he was not coming back for therapy with me and demanded to see someone who he could talk to and who would listen properly. I said that he needed a therapist who could understand and take seriously how overwhelmed and unsupported he felt with his own and his daughter's difficulties.

Mr. O. went on to emphasise how long he had been waiting for help and how little he had received. I said that I thought he felt humiliated by coming for help and being treated by somebody he felt was so detached and uncaring. He calmed down a little and said that no sooner did he find someone he could talk to than he was moved on. I said that he had made a connection with his previous therapist, only to find that he was pushed on to me, who he believed was less skilled and less sensitive. The patient calmed down a little more. I went on to say I thought that behind the accusations and aggression towards me for failing to live up to his expectations, there was a feeling of disappointment in himself for failing to live up to his ideals of self-sufficiency and that perhaps he felt bullied and persecuted by his shortcomings.

Mr. O. then explained that he needed some treatment for his eczema, but that the steroids he needed interfered with his mood. I responded by saying that I thought he needed me to understand that the psychodynamic treatment he needed also inflamed him, especially when he felt I was insensitive to his feelings of humiliation. He said, "Well they say that about some cancer treatments—that the treatment is sometimes more painful than cancer." He then went on to talk about his difficulty in tolerating any feelings of humiliation.

In the case of Mr. O., we can see how his loud complaint and criticism of me provoked my interpretation about his wish to be heard by his previous therapist in an attempt to shame him into lowering his voice. This defensive response from me inflamed him and led to him dramatically leaving the session. The patient was aware that he needed treatment, but he also needed to feel that the person treating him was aware of the fact that the treatment caused him pain. He had very little tolerance for his shortcomings and feelings of humiliation. Indeed, I think he always felt he was unfavourably measuring up against an ideal of himself. This dynamic was projected into me when I failed to live up to his expectations, and his harsh criticism excited my feelings of shame and humiliation in relation to my colleague. Not only was a part of his internal world projected into me through his actions, but it found a suitable home in me because of my sensitivities in this area. When I was able to step back and reflect on what happened, I was able to convey my understanding of his point of view, including his perception of me, to him. This containment then allowed us to recover from the breakdown in our relationship and deepen our understanding of his difficulties.

Case example 3: Responding to psychotic forces in the counter-transference

Betty Joseph (1975) described how the patient could project an aspect of their internal world into the therapist. This is a particular issue with patients who act out in self-destructive ways, as the power of the psychotic communication can interfere with the therapist's objectivity.

In the following example, I will describe Ms. H., a patient I saw in twice-weekly psychotherapy. She had a voice in her head that insisted she was a disgusting pig, with no point to her life, and she should therefore kill herself. She would often try to persuade me that this was a perfectly reasonable position to hold. At other times she feared that her mind had been taken over by a murderous part of herself that would not be satisfied until she was dead. At times she spoke as if she was identified with this voice and at other times she talked as if she was the victim of the voice.

Herbert Rosenfeld (1971) described a group of patients who employed powerful primitive defences against psychic pain associated with vulnerability and dependence. These defences operated like an internal mafia gang that offers protection from psychic pain in return for devotion. Sometimes these internal figures appear in dreams, offering drugs or violent solutions to problems; at other times they take the form of voices that tell the patient what to do.

Ms. H. lived under the sway of a psychotic internal gang that would encourage her to kill or damage herself. At times, when the psychotic internal gang was in the ascendancy, the non-psychotic part was projected into her body, where its influence could be controlled, disowned, and attacked (Lucas, 2009). In this state of mind, she communicated her internal conflict by action. The extreme self-harming and repetitive suicidal behaviour provided an intoxicating, omnipotent internal solution to avoid the pain of emotionally traumatic situations in her life.

During Ms. H.'s treatment, I often felt impotent in the face of the terrifying strength of her self-harming. This powerful communication, which was sometimes enhanced by the sight of her scarred body, had a profound effect on me in the counter-transference. Anxiety caused by the very real threat to the patient's life, as well as the threat to any positive developments made through her involvement with the therapy, made me abandon the analytic attitude of "free-floating attention" (Freud, 1911). From time to time, I would find myself siding with the healthy part of her against the psychotic internal gang. Out of desperation to protect her from her own destructive behaviour, I found myself talking to her as if she was the "good" twin who needed my protection from a jealous twin sister. At other times, I would talk to the jealous twin as if I could employ a powerful therapeutic intervention that could protect the therapy and the patient from the anxieties which provoked self-destructiveness. However, on reflection, I could see that this approach was driven by an unconscious wish to meet the patient's wish for a "God-like figure" who could heroically rescue her from the influence of her murderous internal defences.

It was certainly important to establish a therapeutic relationship with the healthy and receptive part of Ms. H. Indeed, on one occasion she said that my attempts to understand her destructiveness were futile and that the therapy should concentrate on her difficulty with the problem of living. In many ways, I agreed with the patient that her difficulty was in dealing with the feelings of being alive and this is where the therapeutic work needed to take place. As the psychotic gang's sole intention was to destroy her healthy ego, it was not a realistic goal to integrate this structure into the ego. However, once I was able to free myself from the effects of the counter-transference, I was able to understand that the patient was not just the victim of the murderous aspect of herself. When she felt disturbed or upset, she turned to the murderous aspect of her mind as a way of defending herself against ordinary psychic pain. Over time, I began to understand that control over her mind varied according to the level and type of disturbance. At times I had the impression that her mind and capacity to think was completely taken over by the murderous internal gang, while at other times she had a degree of control. My understanding of the counter-transference helped me differentiate between these two states of mind as I began to observe the way I could be pulled into a state of mind where I started to try to advise or coach the patient in an attempt to reduce risk. Therapeutic work with the patient then helped her differentiate between these two states of mind and consequently gain more understanding over the factors that led to self-harming behaviour.

There is a group of patients who communicate their psychological difficulties through persistent and serious self-harm (Evans, 2016). At times the self-harm may involve visible attacks on the body, while at others it can consist of less visible but equally dangerous, often life-threatening, behaviours. As long as they are alive, the life-threatening nature of patients' actions can be denied, while they play Russian Roulette. Anxiety about the threat to life or the damaging nature of their behaviour is often projected, meaning that the responsibility for keeping them alive resides with their family, carers, and mental health services. This can cause those involved to feel tormented, as they carry responsibility for and have a duty of care towards a patient who can treat their life in a careless or reckless way. This dynamic can also get under the skin of professionals, and the patient can be rejected by services because they are either thought to be too risky or deemed to be untreatable. On the other hand, professionals may be immobilised by their counter-transference as they take on responsibility for the patient's behaviour in an unrealistic way. This is often a dynamic that gets played out on in-patient units as the patient projects all responsibility for their behaviour into the staff, who then put the patient on one-to-one observations, while the patient continues to self-harm and act out. This can form a part of a malignantly dependent relationship between staff and patients as the self-destructive behaviour pushes staff to take on more and more responsibility. The relationship can then develop a sado-masochistic element as staff feel understandably persecuted by the patient's self-harming behaviour.

Professionals need to be aware of the tendency to be pulled into either an omnipotent wish to treat the psychosis through rational interpretation or an omnipotent attempt to rescue the patient by acting as if the murderous destructiveness was external to the patient's ego. Both positions deny the underlying dynamic that operates between the psychotic and the non-psychotic part of the patient's ego. While it may not be possible to treat the psychotic part of the mind, its influence needs to be acknowledged. Subtle enactments in the counter-transference are inevitable in the therapeutic relationship, but psychoanalytic supervision can help reduce the pull towards destructive enactments, as well as deepening the understanding of the clinical issue behind the enactment. As in the case of Ms. H., I could see the way my helplessness led to a narrowing of my clinical preoccupations and the loss of my capacity to see the whole clinical picture. Once I was able to free myself from the effects of the counter-transference, I was able to re-establish a truly therapeutic alliance. This involved understanding the relationship between the part of her that wanted help and the part that controlled her through bullying and self-harm.

Case example 4: The infectious nature of psychotic communications

Bion (1957) described a division in the mind between the psychotic and the non-psychotic parts. The psychotic part of the ego hates all emotional links because they attach the individual to psychic pain. It uses violent projection to get rid of any awareness of painful conflicts. At the same time, the non-psychotic part of the ego has the task of thinking about conflicts associated with emotional pain and psychic meaning. When the psychotic part is in the ascendancy, it can fragment and project the non-psychotic part to undermine an individual's capacity to think about themselves in relation to others.

A community psychiatric nurse presented the case of Ms. Q. to a supervision group. A woman in her late 20s, Ms. Q. had been referred to the psychiatric team by social services. Ms. Q.'s three children ranged in age from 6 to 17 years and all had presented behavioural problems at school. Ms. Q. resented the involvement of social services as she felt they were always trying to undermine her abilities as a mother. She resented their interference and had a particular complaint against a female case officer whom she felt was judgemental and critical. The patient also complained that men were breaking into her flat at night and carving their names on her bed. She said she found evidence of their intrusion in the mornings and often phoned the police to register the break-in. The police said they couldn't find any evidence of breaking and entering.

Ms. Q. had been one of five children brought up by a mother who supported her drug habit through prostitution. She didn't know her father, although she suspected he had been one of her mother's customers. When she was 16, she moved away from her home city with a young man and cut off contact with her family of origin. In this new city, the couple had a child. However, this relationship broke down soon after her daughter's birth on account of her partner's violence towards her. The patient then went on to have a couple of other children by different partners. When the group asked about the fathers of these children, the CPN said that she didn't think they amounted to committed relationships. The CPN said that the patient complained that she was on her own with the children and received no support from any of the children's fathers.

Social services reported that Ms. Q. struggled to cope with her children and was prone to emotional outbursts when she felt overwhelmed. They also complained that she had to be reminded to look after the house and care for the children adequately. Indeed, the children had been on the at-risk register for some time.

The CPN said he was bemused by the patient's belief that her house was being broken into by these men at night. In the supervision group, members asked if there was any evidence of these men breaking in. Ms. Q. had introduced the CPN to the neighbours, who seemed to corroborate the story, although they had never seen the intruders themselves. The CPN said that he didn't know what to believe.

Supervision provides an opportunity to discuss the case away from the persuasive influence of the patient by broadening out the discussion about who the patient is and what they seem to be struggling with. In many ways, the group is a place where staff can develop hypotheses about the patient that can then be tested through further clinical enquiry. The CPN said he had been seeing the patient once a week for several months and the patient looked upon him as a confidante. The patient often spent a long time talking about her grievances towards social services, whom she felt were judgemental about her choice of unsupportive fathers for the children. She got into rows with her eldest daughter who was now getting into trouble with boys and drinking alcohol. He said that she seemed to expect the children to look after her and she complained that they didn't help her around the house and that her eldest daughter spent too much time outside the house.

I thought the patient sounded like an immature woman who had very little capacity to metabolise psychic states and think things through. She lacked any internal model of a mother or father and seemed to have been deprived of care as a child. It is reasonable to hypothesise that her insecurity and desperation for affection may have made her grab hold of anyone who showed an interest. Ms. Q. was clearly desperate to get away from her own mother who had failed to provide the sort of love and care she needed, by attaching herself to the father of her first child. Deprived parents often have children young as they believe the parent-child relationship will make up for what they missed in their own childhood. The problem is the lack of differentiation between the child and the parent which leads to difficulties in separating, as projections are pushed backwards and forwards between parent and child.

It seemed that the CPN was supporting Ms. Q. by paying attention to her feeling of being uncared for. Although he apologised in the group for not challenging her possibly delusional beliefs about the intruders, it was obvious that he was helping her think through her relationships with her children, and by caring for her, he was helping her separate herself from her unrealistic expectations of her children. This seemed to help her manage her relationship with her daughter and the other children in a less conflictual, more thoughtful way.

I suspected that her belief the house was being broken into by men at night was an example of a monosymptomatic delusion. The lack of any internal house-mother in her mind meant she was desperate for care but lacked judgement about her objects.

I thought the men that broke into her house at night and carved their names on the bed represented the fathers of her children. These men had broken into her mind and body leaving her with their signature in the form of children who threatened to overwhelm her capacity to cope. Ms. Q. had convinced the neighbours and the CPN that these were real experiences rather than an example of an immature mind that could not manage her responsibilities without support.

Interestingly, the supervision group got concerned about the patient's dependence upon the CPN. We all have concerns and anxieties associated with dependency, attachment, and loss. I sometimes think it's difficult for mental health staff to bear the responsibility of being depended upon. Dependency can be malignant and unhealthy. However, the capacity to depend on others when we are ill and vulnerable is also a sign of health. I tend to think the current mental health culture with its emphasis on recovery and short-term treatments can misdiagnose healthy dependence as pathological, rather than seeing it as an essential aspect of good care. My own view was that the CPN seemed to be playing an extremely important role for this very vulnerable woman. Her immaturity would mean that she would struggle to separate her needs from her children, and so in helping her, he was also helping her children.

Psychological meaning develops within the context of a relationship with another person. Winnicott (1960) famously said that there was no such thing as a baby, only a mother and baby. The infant relies upon the mother to function as an auxiliary ego for some time. Therapeutic relationships have the potential to gather different aspects of the ego together, by adding an understanding of and meaning to a patient's difficulties. Therapeutic relationships are dynamic and involve the professional in the process of identification with the patient, followed by separation and thought. The counter-transference can provide valuable information about the clinical situation but only once it has been recognised and understood. However, the counter-transference is unconscious and the mental health professional may only become aware that they are enacting something on reflection, and after the event. Inevitably, professionals get caught in the transference as they make projective dyads with the patient. The professional must use their experience gained from training, including his or her therapy, supervision, and knowledge of theory to help the process of reflection. In mental health settings, clinical discussion and supervision can provide a psychological space for thinking by turning the clinician/patient dyad into a triad with the supervisor and/or the supervision group as the third. This can then help the mental health professional develop different ways of thinking about the clinical situation. The psychoanalytic concepts of transference and counter-transference, projective identification, and psychotic and non-psychotic states of mind can help throw light on problems that occur in the cycle of identification and separation that is key to therapeutic work.

Conversely to a view that is sometimes expressed in mental health teams, the healthy dependence inherent in all therapeutic relationships encourages the repetition of infantile relationships in relation to the mental health professional. When this is understood, it can lead to the development of insight, but when it is not understood, it can lead to misunderstandings and re-enactments of a patient's early trauma. This is different to a total projection of all responsibility by the patient into the mental health staff. In the case of Ms. H., this had led to an unhelpful and fruitless repetition in the transference, where I was her rival sister interfering in her life. When I was able to separate myself from the role ascribed to me by the patient and interpret the transference to her, we were able to deepen our understanding of the obstacles to therapeutic work. The psychoanalytic model, which focuses on the transference relationship, aims to turn these obstacles into opportunities for understanding. Understanding the transference relationship is one of the main therapeutic goals of psychoanalytic psychotherapy because it throws light on the influence of archaic structures that operate in the patient's mind. This insight can then help the patient become aware of their tendency to be taken over by archaic ways of relating. I believe that this psychodynamic understanding can also be extremely helpful when trying to optimise therapeutic potential in all therapeutic relationships, be they CPN to patient, social worker to client, support worker to in-patient, or any other dyad in which one party offers psychological support to the other.

Discussion

Patients in disturbed states of mind also project aspects of themselves into the professional to relieve unbearable internal states. These projections are often accompanied by behaviour, which puts pressure on the object to behave in ways which correspond to the projected aspect of the patient's mind. The absence of an adequate model for thinking about the effects of these projections leaves professionals in danger of reacting to unconscious forces without understanding them. This is particularly difficult when the element projected by the patient finds a psychological "hook" within the clinician. Patients often pick up on mental health professionals' characteristic strengths and weaknesses. In the case of Mr. O. (see case example 2), we can see the way I automatically re-projected his shame. This led to a breakdown in the therapeutic relationship. The psychoanalytic notion of projective identification helped me understand the enactment and then separate from my identification with the projection. I was then able to make an adjustment in my approach and deepen our understanding of the patient's emotional state, thus re-establishing the therapeutic relationship.

When thinking about the cause of an incident, staff often get caught up identifying who was responsible—the mental health professional or the patient. The reality is often that both staff and patients can contribute to incidents. For example, the nurse who is rather rule-bound and rigid gets into an argument with a patient who projects rigid aspects of themselves into the nurse. The patient then turns up to the kitchen at 9.10 pm asking to make a cup of tea when they know the kitchen closes at 9 pm. The nurse says, "No, you know the kitchen closes at 9," leading to an argument in which the patient accuses the nurse of being a Nazi who loves being in control.

Professionals need to try to tune in to the psychotic wavelength to support their patients' struggles with psychotic aspects of themselves. Supervision groups supporting this sort of insight can help treatment teams think about conflicts between the psychotic and the non-psychotic parts of the ego, even if the patient is not amenable to psychotherapy. Patients diagnosed as suffering from a non-psychotic condition can demonstrate evidence of what mental health professionals may describe as psychotic thinking. Many patients who suffer from a severe personality disorder are dominated by a psychotic internal gang that threatens any life or development. On this occasion, I am using the term "psychosis" to describe what psychotherapists would describe as psychotic mechanisms rather than psychiatrically defined psychosis. These structures are often experienced as alien objects existing within the patient's mind. Ms. H. presented herself as the victim of these persecutory internal structures. This was understandable as these elements of her mind were destructive to the healthy ego's functioning, and integration into the ego was unrealistic. However, pressure on me in the counter-transference to eradicate the gang through either omnipotent attempts to treat the psychosis or equally unrealistic attempts to disown the psychotic gang through splitting and projection led me to become trapped in the role of heroic rescuer or magical therapist.

When I was able to separate myself from the pull to rescue Ms. H., on the one hand, or cure her psychosis, on the other, I could re-establish a balanced picture of Ms. H. including the dynamic that operated between the healthy ego and the psychotic internal gang. When the omnipotent treatment or splitting breaks down, it can lead to violent acting out. Indeed, the subtle interrelationship between the patient's healthy ego and the psychotic internal gang is treated as if it is an internal alien object. The internal structure may represent a destructive aspect of the patient's mind, but it needs to be thought about and accounted for. Forgetting about the psychotic aspects of the person can lead to violent acting out. Psychoanalytic models can help practitioners thinking about unconscious counter-transferential forces that influence a professional's thinking and approach.

Conclusion

Mental health professionals need opportunities to reflect on their contribution to enactments as this can provide valuable information about the nature of the patient's underlying difficulties. The professionals also need a model for thinking about the intra-psychic and interpersonal dynamics, concrete actions, and acting out, as well as unconscious and conscious communication. Without this deeper understanding, the underlying meaning of communication might be lost, ignored, or responded to in an unhelpful way.

The psychoanalytic model provides mental health professionals with a way of thinking about their patients that will help them to make sense of their experience; it also provides them with a language for describing psychological interactions that take place within therapeutic relationships and for articulating their experience of the patient in an objective and considered way. Psychoanalysis offers a model for thinking about and providing meaning for the anxieties that drive us "out of our minds"(Minne, 2007) and this can reduce the risk of thoughtless action. The insight gained through therapeutic work can help restore and discover healthy aspects of the patient's ego.

References

Bion, W. R. (1957). Differentiation of the psychotic from the non-psychotic personalities. *International Journal of Psychoanalysis, 38*(3–4), 266–275.

Evans, M. J. (2016). Deliberate self-harm: "I don't have a problem dying, it's living I can't stand". In M. Wadell and J. Catty (Eds.), *Making room for madness in mental health: The psychoanalytic understanding of psychotic communication* (pp. 137–156). London: Karnac Books.

Freud, S. (1912). The dynamics of transference. In *The standard edition of the complete psychological works of Sigmund Freud*, Volume 12 (pp. 97–108). London: Hogarth Press.

Joseph, B. (1975). The patient who is difficult to reach. In P. Giovacchini (Ed.), *Tactics and techniques in psychoanalytic therapy* (Vol. 2, pp. 205–216). New York, NY: Jason Aronson.

Klein, M. (1935). A contribution to the psychogenesis of manic depressive states. *International Journal of Psychoanalysis*, *16*, 474–527.

Lucas, R. (2009). Differentiating psychotic process from psychotic disorders. In D. Birksted-Breen (Ed.), *The psychotic wavelength: A psychoanalytic perspective for psychiatry* (pp. 260–279). Hove: Routledge.

Minne, C. (2007). Psychoanalytic aspects to the risk containment of dangerous patients treated in high security. In D. Morgan & S. Ruszcynski (Eds.), *Lectures on perversion and delinquency: The portman papers* (pp. 59–82). London: Karnac Books.

Rosenfeld, H. A. (1971). A clinical approach to the analytic theory of the life and death instinct: An investigation into the aggressive aspects of narcissism. *International Journal of Psychoanalysis*, *52*(2), 169–178.

Winnicott, D. W. (1960). The theory of the parent-infant relationship. *International Journal of Psychoanalysis*, *41*, 585–595.

Chapter 5

Psychoanalytic understanding of depression and suicidal risk

Suicide occurs when a person intentionally brings about his or her death. Parasuicide is a non-fatal act of self-injury (for example, taking an overdose that doesn't cause death). Some patients experience suicidal thoughts and impulses in response to a crisis, while others have a long-standing relationship with their suicidal thoughts. A third group of patients may develop a suicidal attitude towards their life while denying active thoughts of suicide.

In recent times a policy of "zero tolerance" towards suicide has been implemented by many mental health trusts. This policy has been implemented despite the unavoidable flaws in risk assessment, not to mention the year-on-year cuts in mental health resources. Although clinicians and clinical teams can learn from suicides and implement best practice wherever practicable, the demand for "zero tolerance" on suicide is driven by an unrealistic demand for ideal mental health services. This demand puts services under an unrealistic and persecutory pressure. The patient's wish to be ideal is met with our own psychotic system which cannot tolerate weakness or limitation. This unachievable demand for suicide-free services persecutes the staff and the institutions who employ them, in the same way as the patient persecutes and blames themselves for their shortcomings. Development in the mental health system is undermined by the tendency to blame individuals and/ or services when they fail to achieve unrealistic goals. This causes demoralisation and cynicism in staff, which then undermines patient care. Rather, it seems to me that services should aspire to reasonable standards of clinical practice while accepting that clinicians are human and prone to mistakes. The attitude should always be one of learning from mistakes rather than blame. Whilst all serious incident enquiry teams espouse this learning attitude, staff often still feel persecuted.

Assessment of suicidal risk

There are two types of risk assessment: the actuarial and the clinical. The biggest predictor of future behaviour is past behaviour. In clinical terms, individuals most at risk of suicide are those who have made repeated attempts in the past or have a family history of successful suicide (Cassells et al. 2005; Kessler et al. 1999; Mann et al. 2006; Nock et al. 2008).

However, in conjunction with the life history of the patient, actuarial profiles using the individual's epidemiology can provide a statistical risk profile. So, for example, men are more likely to kill themselves than women; young and old men are at higher risk than middle-aged men (Samaritans, 2018). Individuals who are socially isolated are at higher risk than those who are valued members of a community. For example, marriage, work, and active relationships with family members all tend to act as protective factors, while the unmarried, the unemployed, and the socially isolated have an increased risk profile, as do those with a history of childhood maltreatment.

While the data helps us fit individuals into high-, medium-, or low-risk groups, of course it cannot provide an indication of which individuals are going to act on their suicidal ideation and actually commit suicide. Actuarial risk profiles, therefore, should only be used as a peripheral guide in the assessment of a patient's risk of suicide as they give a picture of what is going on at the group level, but do not tell you anything about the individual case. The critical issue for clinicians is how the individual in front of you perceives and experiences their circumstances. One way forward might be to combine what we know about an individual's risk factors with what we can glean about the psychological makeup of the individual and their present mental state.

There is disagreement in the literature about the incidence of mental illness in suicide and parasuicide. Some studies say that up to 50% of patients who try to commit suicide are suffering from a formal psychiatric illness, while others put the figure as low as 30%. All studies agree that mental illness increases the risk of suicide. In general, people are more likely to harm themselves, or others, when their state of mind is disturbed. This is because a person's capacity to make rational decisions is impaired; hence alcohol and drugs also increase the risk of deliberate self-harm and suicide, as intoxicated states interfere with judgement.

In conclusion then, a good clinical risk assessment is based upon a combination of the individual's actuarial profile, a clinical assessment of the individual's mental state, and a dynamic formulation that includes the role suicide plays in the patient's internal world.

Therapeutic engagement

After an act of parasuicide, the mental health professional needs to assess the degree to which the patient continues to be a suicide risk and whether they have a current suicide plan. On examination, patients often deny the seriousness of the act.

For example, when I asked one patient who had taken 100 paracetamol now being treated on a medical Intensive Care Unit (ICU) to tell me what had happened, she said, "It wasn't really serious."

If the clinician colludes with the pressure to avoid painful discussion about the seriousness of the act, it will leave the individual on their own with their conflicts and emotional difficulties. It is important for clinicians to resist the temptation to join the individual in minimising the seriousness of the suicidal act. One way to do this is to establish a detailed account of the events that led up to the act. It is also important to identify the "trigger factor." Why did this individual decide to act *then*—what was "the straw that broke the camel's back"? The "trigger factor" often links historical trauma with current trauma in the individual's life. When a patient is vague about their motive, or minimises the seriousness of the parasuicide, they may (unconsciously or consciously) be avoiding exposure to painful emotional truths.

A relationship crisis or loss precipitates most suicidal acts, as an individual's defences are punctured by emotions that threaten to overwhelm the mind. The act of self-harm or attempted suicide aims to evacuate these overwhelming emotions and regain control of their mind through action. It is important to assess the patient as soon as possible after the event so that the raw emotions which provoked the act are still present. Early assessment increases the likelihood of the assessor making emotional contact with underlying issues that provoked the suicidal action. Inevitably, if too much time passes, the individual is able to re-establish their defences and conceal the underlying dynamics and conflicts which caused the parasuicide in the first place. It may feel counter-intuitive or unkind, but in my experience the sooner the patient can be interviewed the better, in order to enable the assessor to get as close as possible to the underlying psychic structure of the mind.

Professionals also need to ascertain whether the patient is in touch with the seriousness of their suicidal state of mind. Some patients remain detached from any concern about themselves and deny the severity of their suicidal intent, yet remain a suicide risk. In this situation, the professional's intuition can indicate that something is going on beneath the surface. The point of the assessment is to ascertain the individual's personality structure and unconscious motivations, in addition to assessing the suicidal risk. Sometimes the conscious explanation is used to conceal an underlying reason touching on painful areas of vulnerability within the individual's personality.

Case example 1: Pre-suicidal state—breakdown of an illusion

As stated above, acts of deliberate self-harm are usually triggered by a loss and subsequent breach of the patient's defences. This breach exposes the individual to feelings of humiliation and rejection. For example, Mr. R., a 30-year-old man, took a large overdose after his wife left him, saying he did not know if he could live without her and wanted to hurt her as much as she had hurt him.

This man couldn't bear the feelings of loss and humiliation associated with the break-up of his marriage. This attempted suicide seemed to be designed to deal with feelings of being unwanted and rejected by forcing his wife to feel guilty in the hope that she would return to the marriage. It was also a way of punishing her for leaving him by saying, "There—look what your actions made me do."

For other people, a catastrophic loss of self-esteem can be caused by the collapse of a business, a relationship, or a view of themselves.

Case example 2: Collapse of an illusion

Ms. S., a 55-year-old unmarried woman, worked as an executive in a small company. She had phoned her ex-boss on a Sunday telling him that she had taken an overdose. He called the ambulance and the patient was admitted to the medical Intensive Care Unit.

The liaison psychiatrist met Ms. S. on a medical ward after she was discharged from the ICU in order to assess her mental state and assess her suicide risk. She asked the patient to give an account of the events leading up to her overdose. The patient maintained there was no particular reason for the timing and that she had thought of suicide for many years. The psychiatrist felt that she was keeping her and the events at a distance, by withholding details and presenting the story in this vague way.

When asked to talk about her family, the patient said that her mother had died when she was young. As the eldest of three sisters, she took on the mother's role and, "Since that time I've always looked after others." The psychiatrist commented on the fact that she seemed to take her mother's place rather than mourn her mother's loss. The patient said that her father never talked about her mother's death and she suspected he had difficulty coming to terms with his grief. She went on to explain that she didn't feel she could mourn her mother's death as she was trying to support her father and her sisters.

The psychiatrist asked Ms. S. about her relationship history. She said that she found it hard to allow anyone to get close to her and that she hadn't had any long-term relationships. However, she said she felt married to her work, explaining that she had been her boss's assistant for the last 30 years. "This is probably the reason I never married." At this point, she started to weep, saying she felt her world had fallen apart since he told her of his retirement date. The psychiatrist then commented on the loss of this important working relationship and asked her about other friends or hobbies. It became apparent that she had very little in her life apart from her work, so her devotion to her boss seemed to repeat the role she played in her family when her mother died. Ms. S. continued weeping while saying that on the day of the overdose (a Sunday), she had texted her boss asking to meet. He had said that he wasn't able to. She confessed to the psychiatrist that she and the boss (who was married) had been having an affair for many years and often met on Sundays, using work as a pretext. Indeed, the overdose took place on the first Sunday after her boss retired, having told her he would no longer be able to visit her. She said, "I sacrificed my life for him and now he is going to dump me for his wife."

Ms. S. had started the consultation by denying the seriousness of her actions and trying to keep the psychiatrist away from the areas of emotional pain. Although she mentioned the fact that she had thought about suicide for many years, she did not indicate the link between these thoughts and the events that triggered her suicidal actions.

When assessing a suicidal patient, the assessor needs to understand the pre-suicidal psychic structure, including the unconscious phantasies and relationships that support their psychic equilibrium. Campbell and Hale (2017) highlight the importance of the *core complex* in suicidal states. The nub of the *core complex* is that the individual has phantasies of merging with an ideal object—in unconscious phantasy this is the mother who once upon a time *could* solve all the infant's problems. This phantasy acts as a psychic retreat from painful psychic reality. The suicidal phantasies are provoked because the individual feels betrayed by their ideal object. In the clinical example above, the patient had told the nurse that after her mother's death, she had become "the woman of the house." Thus she took her mother's place and in doing so lost her position as her parent's daughter. This was accompanied by an illusion of her being her father's partner in helping him look after her two younger sisters. In fantasy, she became her father's ideal support who sacrifices her position as a child, along with her own developmental needs, in order to support her father and her siblings in his grief.

Although the history gives a picture of Ms. S.'s psychic structure, it does not explain how this psychic structure was being played out in her current life and what relevance it plays in relation to the act. Further examination of the facts leading up to the attempted suicide (the overdose) reveals the way the historical facts are repeated in her current life as she developed an illusion that she was the boss's ideal partner. This illusion breaks down when the boss finally texts her to say he will not be visiting on the Sunday after his retirement. She takes the overdose to punish her boss for the breakdown in the illusion: "I sacrificed my life for him and now he is going to dump me for his wife." In this way, she was trying to force her ex-boss to re-establish the arrangement, as she does not feel she can bear the loss of the illusion. The trigger factor of "the boss's text" acts as "the straw that breaks the camel's back," provoking a projection of desire and vulnerable aspects of the self into the body that is then hated and disowned. This paves the way for suicidal ideation and the suicidal act which plans to triumph over painful feelings and punish the ideal object for letting them down.

When assessing patients after an attempted suicidal, it is important to consider the unconscious as well as the conscious meanings associated with the act. If the suicidal fantasy is not understood and worked through, the individual remains in danger of resorting to suicide as a means of dealing with their conflict, pain, and anxiety. Freud (1920) described the way internal conflicts that have not been made conscious are enacted and re-enacted by the individual. He coined the term "repetition compulsion" to describe the way these unconscious conflicts emerge as actions until they have been consciously understood. This process is often evident in acts of suicide and parasuicide, as unconscious phantasies and conflicts are repeated in the individual's current life. The link is often revealed by the trigger which links the current situation to historical facts. This understanding can then illuminate the relationship between the individual's psychic structure and their suicidal action.

Case example 3: Pressure on the clinician to be the ideal object

Suicidal thoughts and fantasies are often provoked by a breakdown in phantasies associated with ideal solutions. These breakdowns expose grievances against parental objects that patients feel have failed to provide perfect care. This pattern can be repeated in adult life as they seek ideal relationships that they believe will repair damaged aspects of themselves. They find it hard to accept that all relationships are fallible and involve some frustration and disappointment.

A liaison psychiatrist referred the case of Mrs. T., a 38-year-old married woman who took an overdose of medication following a visit to see her aunt in hospital. The medical doctor responsible for her aunt's care told the patient there was nothing more the hospital could do and the aunt would be discharged so she could die at home. The patient stormed out of the hospital, took a large overdose, and then phoned her daughter to tell her what she had done. In her parasuicide assessment interview, she said her daughter was leaving home to go to university and she couldn't face having to look after her aunt. After making an initial assessment, the liaison psychiatrist concluded that the patient was a fragile woman with long-standing grievances and anxieties about separation. The liaison psychiatrist decided that these long-standing difficulties would benefit from a longer-term approach and referred her on for a psychotherapy consultation.

When l met Mrs. T., I told her that the meeting was a psychotherapy consultation to see if we thought psychotherapy could help her with her difficulties. I explained that we might meet a few times as part of the consultation, but I would not be offering the psychotherapy myself. I then asked her to tell me why she felt she needed psychotherapy. She immediately replied that she didn't know why she was here and that as the professional, she thought it was my job to tell her what she needed. I said that she wanted me to prescribe her some treatment and that she would then fit in as expected with the expectation that the treatment prescribed would cure the problem. The patient looked angry and said that she thought I was supposed to be the expert. I pointed out the way she wanted me to tell her what to do, as if I would know what was best for her, while she needed to take no active part in the decision-making. She replied by saying, "What is the point in talking if you can't do anything about the problem?" I replied that I thought it was important to try and understand what she was thinking and feeling rather than come up with a plan of action per se. At this point in the interview, Mrs. T. broke down in tears saying that she had always been close to her aunt and couldn't bear the thought of her dying. I said that I thought she had to believe that someone could cure her aunt and it frightened her to think that there may be limits to what could be done.

After this she became calmer. I asked Mrs. T. to tell me something about her history. She was the second of five children and had been brought up by her grandmother in her country of origin after her parents had moved to England when she was two years old. She didn't feel her parents were interested in her and didn't feel any warmth towards them after joining them in this country when she turned 11. She told me a dream in which she blew up her family house with all the family in it and went on to say that she was furious with her daughter who showed no gratitude for the sacrifices she had made. She also told me how useless the psychiatrist was and that he was just like her aunt's doctor who had said there was no more treatment available for her aunt.

I suggested she was trying to push me into saying I could take away her difficulties and provide her with an ideal solution. But that if I didn't, she would accuse me of letting her down as she felt the psychologist and the doctor had let her and her aunt down. She replied she was not very optimistic that I would be able to help her and went on to explain, with pride, how she never relied on anyone to help her because people always let her down.

Towards the end of the consultation, I said that I thought Mrs. B. was furious with her parents, whom she felt had failed to care for her. Instead, she saw herself as becoming the ideal parental figure that sacrificed everything in the care of others. However, she got angry when her devotion and care was not able to prevent her daughter's wish to leave home, or cure her aunt's cancer. I was struck by the lack of reference to Mrs. T.'s marriage or her husband, so I asked her about her husband. The patient said that her husband was pretty useless and that she didn't even think of bothering him.

In the second interview, Mrs. B. told me how angry she was because another member of staff promised to do something for her but failed to make further contact. I said that I also thought she believed I had failed to take the pain of her problem away, leaving her with feelings about her aunt's illness and her daughter's separation, while waiting for the next session. She said that it reminded her of her experience of childhood when she waited for her parents to contact her and invite her to join them in England. I said I thought she harboured powerful wishes to punish them. She described coldly how she had got back at them by cutting off contact when she gave birth to her daughter.

Towards the end of the consultation, I invited Mrs. B. to discuss treatment options and reminded her that I could put her on the waiting list for psychotherapy. The patient became angry again saying I should tell her what to do and she didn't see why she should be invited to discuss treatment options. Again, she threatened to leave if I didn't tell her what to do. She said that I was useless and that no one did anything to help. I said that waiting for a treatment vacancy felt very harsh and cruel as it left her with difficult feelings about separation and loss. At that point in the interview, Mrs. B. shouted that I should stop talking about separation, as she could not bear thinking about separations as it made her feel bleak.

Mrs. T.'s case illustrates some of the problems that can underlie acts of deliberate self-harm, as she created ideal relationships in her mind with objects that would never leave her. Restricting her view of reality and controlling the nature of her relationships sustained these illusions. Any relationship that threatened to undermine her illusions was treated as failed ideal objects. For example, when the doctor told her nothing more could be done for her aunt, she felt betrayed and let down in a way that threatened the collapse of her ego. The overdose was an attempt to control and punish the people she felt had let her down.

Lucas (2009) highlights the importance of thinking about the psychotic and the non-psychotic parts of the mind when thinking about suicide. Bion (1957) differentiated between the psychotic and the non-psychotic parts of the personality. The psychotic part hates all emotional links and attacks the ego's capacity to perceive and register emotional links while the non-psychotic part is aware of the significance of relationships and registers their emotional significance. In depressive states, the psychotic part of the ego wants to form a powerful alliance with an ideal "God-like" object that is all-knowing and all-powerful to counter the force of the depressive feelings. In the case of Mrs. T., this is the God-like doctor or therapist she has set up in her mind to remove the pain of death and separation. She sets up a contract in her mind where she submits herself to the ideal objects who, in her phantasy, narcissistically demand to be worshipped in return for protection from painful realities. The ideal object is threatened with accusations of carelessness and impotence if they fail to agree to the terms of the contract. Ordinary vulnerabilities and limitations are believed to be intolerable and a sign of weakness rather than a sane assessment of the situation.

Mrs. T. put a lot of pressure on me to act as if I knew the answer to her difficulties and could prescribe a solution, which she would passively comply with. In this way, she was the passive recipient of treatment while I was the "all-knowing expert." This behaviour was enacted at the start of the session as she tried to get me to tell her what to do as if I held the answer to her difficulties. She again tried the same operation at the end of the second session, as I had said I would not be continuing to see her. In this way, her relationships with carers are divided between the ideal figures who prescribe the solution and those that fail to tell her what to do and are consequently useless.

Freud's contemporary, the physician Stekel, proposed that anyone who kills themselves has wanted to kill another or wished the death of another (Stekel, 1910). The fundamental truth of this statement has persisted throughout the development of psychodynamic and psychoanalytical perspectives on suicide. Freud theorised that murderous impulses against others are turned on one's self and precipitate suicidal thoughts. In his paper "Mourning and Melancholia" (Freud, 1917), Freud describes how, "The shadow of the object falls upon the ego." By this he means that the ego solves the problem of a person out there in the world treating them badly, by bringing the external object into the ego so it becomes an "internal object." Once internalised, the ego can torture the object forever. Hence the melancholic lament of, "I am so awful, I should be dead, I am worthless." The ego is talking not about itself per se, but about the internalised object which has now let it down (as it presumably did in the past) and with whom it is so angry. So angry in fact that the ego wishes this internalised, hated object dead. In suicide, so the psychoanalytic theory argues, the hated object is killed off. But, unfortunately, so is the rest of the ego. Both ego and "internal object" end up dead.

Mrs. T. tries to push the clinician to become the ideal object that could take away her pain by providing a magical solution. She makes it clear that I will join the other failed objects in her life, like her husband and her aunt's doctor and originally her parents, if I refuse to live up to her expectations. Thus, when I point out that I cannot cure her and she will have to wait for treatment, she becomes furious. Any separation from the ideal object is experienced as a betrayal and something that therefore needs to be attacked. So, unlike most parents who see it as a sign of success that their children can separate and go to university, Mrs. T. feels it represents a breakdown in her ideal relationship with her daughter. If her daughter needs to move away from her in order to get on with her life, it must represent a failing in her as a mother.

Case example 4: The role of unconscious phantasy in the therapeutic relationship

A liaison psychiatric nurse presented the case of Mr. V., a 20-year-old man in supervision. Apparently, he had concealed from his mother (who was in the house at the time) the fact that he had taken a large amount of paracetamol. She only became aware of this when he became critically ill as a result of his overdose. When the liaison nurse commented on the fact that he had not told his mother he had taken the overdose until it was nearly too late, he said that he hadn't decided whether he was going to tell her or not. The nurse said that she thought he was very angry with his mother and seemed to want to punish her by taking an overdose in the house and not telling her. Mr. V. said that was not the case and explained that he was aware that he needed to get medical treatment within 12 hours to avoid life-threatening liver damage. However, he went on to say that he needed to be dangerously ill for his parents to appreciate the severity of his distress and emotional state. The nurse commented on the fact that he had to force his parents to take notice. He complained that although his parents had been able to put their lives back together since his brother's death from liver cancer several years ago, he himself had failed to come to terms with his sibling's death. With some resentment, he said that his sense of being stuck was in contrast to his parent's lively re-engagement with life, which he didn't understand. He said that it was as if his brother's death had never happened and he was angry about the fact that his parents didn't seem to notice his difficulty coming to terms with his loss. The nurse asked the patient to tell her what had triggered the overdose and he said that he had discovered two days before that his chosen university had rejected him after he had failed his exams for the second time. Mr. V. told the nurse that he struggled to study since his brother's death and all his dreams and aspirations seemed to have collapsed.

The nurse asked Mr. V. to tell her something about his relationship with his brother. He said he had always looked up to him and wanted to emulate him. With a note of sarcasm, he said that hadn't included getting into the same Intensive Care Unit as a result of liver problems. He went on to explain that his brother was treated on the same unit for his liver cancer as he had been for his overdose.

Unconscious phantasy has an effect on behaviour and this is particularly evident when the individual's ego is overwhelmed by painful emotions. We can see the phantasy of Mr. V. joining his brother to avoid feelings of separation and loss, in order to evade his grief. Freud (1917) describes in "Mourning and Melancholia" the way the individual takes the lost object into the ego and forms an identification in order to avoid feelings of separation and loss. Thus, in Freud's words, mourning is avoided by internalising the dead object which then takes residence in the patient's mind. As he wrote, "The shadow of the object falls upon the ego." The lost object is then idealised and protected from all criticism. It is interesting to note that a eulogy does not criticise but only praises the deceased. Split-off aspects of the self and the object that do not match up to the idealised view are then projected into unwanted aspects of the self. The split ego now lives in relation to its parts as an ideal self partly identified with the ideal dead object who sits in judgement and triumphs over the actual self that is seen as full of human failings. When you listen to melancholic patients it sometimes feels like listening to someone bullying themselves; "I should have visited him in hospital, I didn't deserve him, he was a saint." You can hear the identification with a saint-like figure condemning them as a person with human frailties.

Mr. V. demonstrates his difficulty in coming to terms with his brother's death because he has formed an unconscious, internal identification with him. Indeed, as a result of his overdose, he perhaps calculates that he will end up with a liver complaint on the same ICU his brother stayed on. He has incorporated a picture of his brother into his ego ideal which then sits in judgement over selfish, greedy, and unwanted aspects of himself which he might describe as his wish to pass his exams, or go to university and live the rest of his life without his brother being able to. To avoid the guilt associated with these unwanted aspects of himself, he projects them into the parents who are punished for letting go of his brother and getting on with their lives. In actual fact, they have simply managed to get on with a normal mourning and not get caught in a pathological one. Mr. V.'s punitive attitude towards his parents feels justified, as he believes they are guilty of betraying his brother and therefore him as he has internalised his brother—a case of "I'll eat you up, I love you so." He then forces them to re-experience being at the bedside of a seriously ill son, as if he wants to take the family back to the moments leading up to, but just before, his brother's death.

The suicidal act itself reveals a significant confusion between the body and the mind, for it reveals the patient's reduced capacity to know reality, while the body is used to get rid of extreme states of mind. Psychoanalytic theory argues that the body represents the hated primary caregiver (mother) who is always the ideal object that needs to be punished for her failings. In the case of Mr. V., we can see how his cruel indifference to his body and his life is used as a reproach to his mother. In phantasy, he gambles with the idea that his mother will find him unconscious and feel appropriately guilty for getting on with her life. His sense of triumph accompanies the conscious fantasy of his mother finding his unconscious body. However, the patient tells us how, "They will be forced to recognise the extent of my difficulties when I become physically ill as a result of the overdose" and then he can punish them for their oversights; "Then they will be sorry." Grievances and a wish to punish failed ideal objects often form part of the motivation for parasuicide and suicide. Campbell (1995) believes the unconscious suicide phantasy is a "psychotic phantasy," because the individual believes that the attack on their own body will *not* result in their death, as an observing part of the self will survive. For example, I think Mr. V. believed his parents might be so shocked to find his dead body, they would mend their ways. In phantasy, he believed that this might make his life bearable.

Case example 5: States of chronic suicidality

There are a group of patients that demonstrate a suicidal attitude towards life that is evident of a neglectful or damaging attitude towards their health.

I saw Mr. W. for once-weekly psychotherapy in the NHS after he became severely depressed and actively suicidal, following a heart attack and subsequent loss of his job as a successful professional. He was the older of two children and his mother suffered from post-natal depression after his birth. Due to the mother's second bout of post-natal depression, following the birth of his brother, he was sent to live with an aunt. He reported that he always felt his brother was the favourite and he could never gain the approval from his parents. He told me his mother said that with all his many opinions, he reminded her of a "toddler with a missile" while she viewed his brother as easy-going and warmer. He did well at school and trained in law using his sharp logical intellect to defend clients whom he believed were victims of an over-critical legal system. Although he was very successful and proud of his achievements at work, the patient was dogged by a feeling that he could not measure up to his own, or his parents', particularly his mother's, expectations.

During our first meeting, he said that although he was good at his job, he believed he was a failure as a man and that his life was not worth living. Mr. W. was married and he freely admitted relying heavily upon his wife and their two grown-up children. He had an adversarial manner and tried to keep his emotions out of the therapy, arguing that they had nothing to do with his problems or attitude towards his life. This attitude of chronic suicidality was reflected in his attitude towards his physical health as he took no interest in the way his obesity affected his heart. His suicidality was also apparent in the sessions as he maintained that without work, he had no purpose in life. At times it felt as if we were in a court room battle with him employing his powerful logic to defeat a rather inferior prosecuting barrister.

When I tried to point out his irritation with my approach, he denied it, saying that he was just no good at psychotherapy and that he was sure I must know what

I was doing. My response to him was that he seemed uncomfortable acknowledging any critical thoughts or feelings towards me, but looked more comfortable blaming any fault in the therapy on himself. Mr. W. often sunk into a defiant silence giving me very little material to work with and appeared detached from any sense of concern about himself or the state of his life. Beneath the submissive attitude towards the therapy and his life, I felt there was a competitive attitude towards himself and his difficulties that refused to allow or permit any feelings of attachment or dependence. After some time, I took up the detached attitude towards his difficulties in life as a form of suicidality in response to my failure to help him. The patient took great exception to this, saying that I had completely misunderstood and his lack of interest in life was a rational response in general to his relative failure in life.

I was often provoked by his negativity and provocative attacks on my attempts to help and the therapy could descend into something resembling a "court room drama" rather than psychotherapy as I tried to argue with his nihilistic logic. When this happened, I was aware that in hindsight I had lost my therapeutic setting. Mr. W. was far more comfortable arguing with me than working with me, as this threatened to expose his underlying feelings of vulnerability.

Mr. W. was never consciously critical of his parents for their treatment of him. However, we can see how he projected his vulnerability and sense of injustice into the clients he defended. Indeed, he would never argue for any value in himself, but he did identify worth in protecting those he represented. When his nihilism provoked me, he would mock my professional distance and superiority. In this way, I became the heartless mother that judged him harshly and failed to see his underlying hurt and vulnerability. His father was guilty of standing by and never stepping in to protect his son from his wife's harsh treatment.

I assessed that Mr. W. suffered depression at an early age as a result of the separation from his mother due to her post-natal depression. It may well be that he was conscious of her fragility and knew she found it difficult to deal with his anger and disappointment when they were reunited. Deep-seated feelings of rage and frustration had to be directed towards the self to protect his internal object (the object being his relationship to his mother on whom he depended for survival) and so he developed a melancholic internal structure—a structure in which his aggression towards the failed ideal object could never be expressed and mourned but was continually directed towards the self. In other words, he internalised a punishing maternal object which he identified with. I think his resentment towards his mother for her favouritism towards the brother and her critical attitude towards him, as well as his father for failing to protect him was enacted through his defence of his clients. Consequently, his job functioned like an antidote for his rather self-destructive internal structure.

Mrs. O'Shaughnessy (1999) has described the dominance of an ego-destructive superego in the mind of a patient with psychotic depression. The superego has a sado-masochistic relationship with the ego and attacks it in a sadistic way. Mr. W. did something similar because he had internalised the unloved and unlovable child who was always a disappointment, while protecting the ideal picture of his parents that could not be faulted, but who sat in judgement over this unforgivable, disappointing child. In this way, he felt that he could never live up to the parental expectations that existed in his mind and the ordinary child, full of imperfections and problems, was both intolerable and unlovable. The denial of aggression and grievance towards a failing figure (his mother as a child and me in the transference) and the adoption of a masochistic position provide a difficult technical issue. Therapeutic interventions, designed to pick up on the hostility which underlies self-hatred and masochism, can be used in turn to endorse the patient's entrenched position: "See I told you I was a bad person and a failure."

In a paper entitled "Time and the Garden of Eden Illusion" Steiner (2019) describes a phantasy of returning to an illusory ideal relationship with the mother. This phantasy is often connected with an ideal time place or relationship in the patient's life before things went wrong. Mr. W. believed that the only worthwhile goal of therapy would be to restore him to what he imagined was a state of bliss before his brother was born and he was separated from his mother. Then he would be able to be the ideal, loving child, free of guilt caused by the resentment and hatred he felt towards his parents. Feelings of need, resentment, and grievance were projected into his body while he moved up into his mind through the development of an intellectualised defence. He then treated his body with complete contempt—much like an abusive parent would treat an unloved, unwanted child. Any observation made by the therapist about his disinterest for his physical state was treated with contempt, just as he identified with the ideal figures in his mind that looked down on his needs and his difficulties. He fitted in with his own harsh assessment of himself in a masochistic acceptance of his inadequacies and faults.

Mr. W. did feel he benefited from the psychotherapy as an academic exercise but resisted any attempt to examine his feelings. He believed I was trying to claim importance and influence if I brought myself into the frame, much as an older child might feel his mother did with a new baby, "Look at me, look at how clever I am with your baby brother." Although after six months of treatment, the patient was no longer actively suicidal, his approach to life could be described as suicide-by-neglect given the seriousness of his heart condition. When his GP told him to lose weight, he complained he couldn't find the motivation, while projecting anxiety about himself into others. My patient needed to find an object that could help him manage and face his rage and disappointment, as well as help him come to terms with his limitations and the unattractive aspects of himself. However, his intellectualised defence meant that he neglected his emotional needs and his defences remained firmly in place.

Some patients put the clinician in the position of being responsible: "Well my life does not mean anything to me, so I can do whatever I want, but you are responsible." This can become part of a sado-masochistic dynamic between the therapist and the patient in longer-term therapeutic relationships, as the patient pulls the clinician into a situation where the therapist may try to rescue the patient from his/her relationship with a destructive internal figure. The patient may then self-harm to punish the therapist for failing to provide ideal care or a magical solution.

After the heart attack and loss of his professional life, Mr. W. sunk into a melancholic attitude towards life, insisting he was a failure who did not measure up to his standards. Typically, as our work was coming to an end, he told me he was considering seeing someone in private psychotherapy, but then in the last session he said other things had come up that would have to take priority, i.e. he was going to put household expenses before his own needs. He explained how this fitted with a long-term pattern of putting others and their needs before his own. I think he allows this to go on while secretly resenting the fact that his needs are ignored, neglected, and put to the back of the queue. The anger towards others who have failed to help him is expressed via his attitude towards his own neglected physical state. Again, if we think of the split between the psychotic and the non-psychotic parts of the mind, we can see how Mr. W. fits in with the melancholic wish to submit himself to an ideal figure who will provide a solution to all of life's pain. He has a view of himself as being identified with God's helper—someone who devotes himself to the care of others and has no needs of his own. Understanding the oscillations between the psychotic and the non-psychotic parts of the mind helps us make sense of the dynamic interchange between a part that acknowledges the need for help and another that wants to kill off the needy part for existing at all. My attempts to engage Mr. W.'s non-psychotic mind to think about how this system starves him of proper attention and care then provokes the psychotic part of him into mocking me with contempt. On one occasion, this defence broke down in a dramatic way when I suggested we end the therapy as a result of his continued attacks. He broke down in tears saying that he would be left without any support if I ended the therapy. I think this was a reaction from his non-psychotic part that was frightened of being left to cope alone with his murderous, rageful psychotic self.

Discussion

In this chapter, I have tried to outline some of the issues involved in the assessment, engagement, and treatment of individuals in suicidal states of mind. I have also illustrated the role of unconscious fantasy in chronic suicidal states of mind. Patients need their clinicians to take acts of suicide and deliberate self-harm seriously, by assessing the individual's personality structure, including their long-term difficulties as well as the acute trigger situation. However, there is often a wish to deny the seriousness of the act as it exposes unconscious motives, vulnerabilities, and long-standing difficulties, which the patient wishes to conceal. If the clinician adopts a calm but firm approach, they can demonstrate that difficult issues can be examined and thought about in a supportive way. It is important that the clinician is sensitive to the feelings of humiliation the patient may feel, without being controlled by them. The patient needs to know that the clinician cares enough to take the trouble to understand their underlying issues, even if this risks exposing painful underlying issues and vulnerabilities.

Having said this, the clinical has to try and guard against retaliation and mockery in response to the individual's tendency to minimise and deny the extent of their difficulties. For example, Mr. W. believed it was normal for him to adopt a fatalistic attitude towards his physical health after his heart attack and the subsequent loss of his profession. He believed he was right to want to die as he felt his failure in life was a rational assessment. We could say his ego had been taken over by the ego ideal which meant his imperfections were intolerable to him. The therapy involved helping the patient understand that his self-assessment was far from "rational" and was instead the consequence of an extremely unforgiving, internal judge who wrongly believed all imperfections were unforgivable. This self-accusation was also unconsciously directed at his parents who he felt had failed to help him overcome his resentment towards his baby brother. To some extent, this underlying structure had remained latent as long as he was working in a high-profile profession where he could project his vulnerability into his clients, then make them better by being a great lawyer, but it became active as soon as he was no longer able to work and lost his source of self-esteem.

Mr. W. had internalised an internal structure which offered him a way of triumphing over psychic pain. His contempt for his own physical health, which he enacted by being obese with a serious heart condition, meant that he couldn't be hurt by any future loss. There is a group of patients who are chronically suicidal; indeed, one might say that these patients can only bear having a relationship with life if they have a powerful relationship with death. These patients often project responsibility for their lives into professionals, while adopting a sadistic attitude towards the help offered. The relationship between staff and patients can become sado-masochistic in such cases, as professionals feel punished by this cruel indifference towards life, causing them to hate the patient back. It may not be possible to stop the patient's relationship with self-destructive patterns of behaviour, but if professionals can work with a patient to understand what drives the relationship with suicidality, they can hope to ameliorate the situation. Or at the very least, they offer the patient support in managing their psychotic, suicidal part.

Conclusion

Clinical supervision is essential when dealing with patients in highly disturbed states of mind as it provides an opportunity to think through the relationship between the patient and the clinician. Although the therapeutic relationship is key in the assessment and treatment of patients in suicidal states of mind, it is inevitably prone to the effects of transference and counter-transference. The clinician will be pushed and pulled in different directions by powerful anti-life forces that can have an effect on judgement and the accurate assessment of risk. Supervision can also help turn clinical impasses and difficulties into further understanding of the patient's psychopathology and their underlying conflicts and phantasies.

References

Bion, W. R. (1957). Differentiation of the psychotic from the non-psychotic personalities. *International Journal of Psychoanalysis*, *38*(3–4), 266–275.

Campbell, D. (1995). The role of the father in a pre-suicidal state. *International Journal of Psychoanalysis*, *76*(2), 315–323.

Campbell, D., & Hale, R. (2017). The core complex. In *Working in the dark: Understanding the pre-suicidal state of mind* (pp. 30–41). London and New York, NY: Routledge.

Cassells, C., Paterson, B., Dowding, D., & Morrison, R. (2005). Long- and short-term risk factors in the prediction of inpatient suicide: A review of the literature. *Crisis*, *26*(2), 53–63. [PubMed] [Google Scholar].

Freud, S. (1917). Mourning and melancholia. In *The standard edition of the complete psychological works of Sigmund Freud*, Volume 14 (pp. 237–259). London: Hogarth Press.

Freud, S. (1920). Beyond the pleasure principle. In *The standard edition of the complete psychological works of Sigmund Freud*, Volume 18. London: Hogarth Press.

Kessler, R. C., Borges, G., & Walters, E. E. (1999). Prevalence of and risk factors for lifetime suicide attempts in the National comorbidity Survey. *Archives of General Psychiatry*, *56*(7), 617–626. [PubMed] [Google Scholar].

Lucas, R. (2009). Education in psychosis. In D. Birksted-Breen (Ed.), *The psychotic wavelength: A psychoanalytic perspective for psychiatry* (pp. 280–299). London: Routledge.

Mann, J. J., Currier, D., Stanley, B., Oquendo, M. A., Amsel, L. V., & Ellis, S. P. (2006). Can biological tests assist prediction of suicide in mood disorders? *International Journal of Neuropsychopharmacology*, *9*(4), 465–474. [PubMed] [Google Scholar].

Nock, M. K., Borges, G., Bromet, E. J., Alonso, J., Angermeyer, M., Beautrais, A., … Williams, D. (2008). Cross-national prevalence and risk factors for suicidal ideation, plans and attempts. *British Journal of Psychiatry*, *192*(2), 98–105. [PMC free article] [PubMed] [Google Scholar].

O'Shaughnessy, E. (1999). Relating to the super ego. *International Journal of Psychoanalysis*, *80*, 861–870. Reprinted in R. Rusbridger (Ed.), *Inquiries in psychoanalysis: Collected papers of Edna O'Shaughnessy*. Hove: Routledge, 2015.

Samaritans. (2018). Retrieved from https://www.samaritans.org/about-samaritans/research -policy/suicide-facts-and-figures/.

Steiner, J. (2019). Time and the garden of Eden illusion. *International Journal of Psychoanalysis*, *99*(6), 1274–1287.

Stekel, W. (1910). Symposium on suicide. In *On suicide* (pp. 33–141). New York, NY: International Universities Press.

Chapter 6

Psychotherapeutic work with emotionally unstable personality disorder

The presentation of patients with a diagnosis of emotionally unstable personality disorder (EUPD), which used to be called borderline personality disorder, can fluctuate rapidly between integrated functioning and fragmented, psychotic states of mind. In crisis, their fragmented states of mind are usually accompanied by actions designed to expel disturbing emotions. These states of mind, which can be dismissed by some as attention-seeking, are alarming and cause severe management problems for psychiatric services, general practitioners, and others. Although this group of patients are, at times, capable of insightful and mature thinking, their mental functioning can deteriorate when faced with psychic conflict as this causes them mental pain. When this happens, such patients may lose their capacity to digest and tolerate the frustrations of psychic reality and fall back on primitive defences. Primitive defences split-off aspects of their ego associated with perception and project these into the body or an external object. These projections, designed to externalise internal conflicts, are often accompanied by dramatic action (acting out).

Consequently, individuals suffering from EUPD find their perception of themselves and others is distorted and this leads to difficulties in differentiating between self and other. When their environment changes and/or they undergo separation from an object into whom they have projected a split-off part of their ego, their psychological equilibrium is upset. They often have a history of highly dependent and/or abusive personal relationships. The projection of important aspects of their internal world can leave them feeling empty and despairing. They can sometimes fill this emptiness with drugs, alcohol, self-harming, or sado-masochistic relationships. They seek excitement as a way of feeling alive and are often demanding of service resources, especially when their self-destructive and chaotic behaviour raises anxiety amongst health-care professionals.

It is common for patients with EUPD to have large numbers of health-care professionals involved at the same time, since many of them are victims of varying kinds of abuse. Telling their painful history is a way to enlist professionals' sympathy and this can stimulate a wish in the professional to rescue them. Such patients seek intense, "special" relationships in which they believe their dependency needs can be met, and they often push staff beyond the bounds of normal professional behaviour in an attempt to meet these needs. Self-harming behaviour can force carers into actions designed to protect the patient from themselves. For example, staff may decide to put a patient under close nursing observation. At times this may be appropriate. However, it can become a malignant cycle, as the patient projects all responsibility for their well-being into the staff. Any attempts to reduce the level of observation leads to acting out, which in turn puts pressure on the staff to increase observations once more. The clinical situation can become stuck, as any progress then produces a negative therapeutic reaction.

Staff can then retreat into a moralistic state of mind in response to an understandably frustrating clinical situation. Planning for discharge from in-patient units may be clinically appropriate, but it is often accompanied by a "judgemental" attitude as discharge is accompanied by a justification which says that the patient "does not have a diagnosable mental illness." This defensive attitude pushes all responsibility for treatment onto the patient as if they could control their disruptive actions and behaviours. Indeed, it is common to hear staff describe patients as a "borderline" or "personality disorder" in a pejorative way that indicates the extent to which the patient has got under their skin. This sort of thinking is based on a false division between something called "personality disorder" and something called "mental illness." The reality is that virtually all presentations of psychiatric illness are derived from disorders in the patient's personality.

When the patient feels blamed or rejected in this way, it can produce an increase in the level of acting out in an attempt to force staff to continue caring for them. I sometimes think that the label of "Borderline" is an indication of the extent to which the patient has been able to negatively affect staff through operation of the counter-transference.

So why do borderline patients have such a disturbing effect on mental health professionals? Using clinical examples to illustrate my ideas, I am going to outline some of the psychoanalytic thinking which I have found helpful when trying to think about, and work therapeutically with, patients in borderline states of mind.

Case example 1: Paranoid-schizoid position

Patients in borderline states of mind employ primitive defences by splitting and projecting aspects of their ego into the external world. Klein (1935, 1940, 1946) differentiated between two major types of psychic functioning. She coined the term "paranoid schizoid position" to describe a state of mind dominated by these primitive psychic defences. These defences are employed to protect the ego from internal conflict and psychic pain. Anxieties in the paranoid-schizoid position are related to a feeling of persecution and a preoccupation with protection of the ego. As the ego develops some strength and capacity to bear psychic pain, the need for primitive defences reduces. The reduction in splitting and projection allows integration to take place; signalled by anxieties about loss and guilt rather than persecution, this more integrated form of psychic functioning Klein defined as the "depressive position."

Ms. X. was a woman in her 40s who was referred to a specialist psychotherapy service for personality-disordered patients. She felt she was a failure in all aspects of her life and was tormented by a belief that she was the cause of all her misfortunes. Although the patient complained that she was useless in a repetitive and circular way, she was also damning of doctors and therapists who had failed to help or cure her over a two-decade history of mental illness.

Ms. X.'s family were all members of a fundamentalist cult who believed that one day God's chosen people would be lifted up into Heaven. She described her father as a difficult man who devoted his life to the care of others less fortunate than himself. Her mother supported her father despite her reservations about the implications of his fundamentalist beliefs on the family. She had an older sister, and a brother who had died of cancer in his 20s. As a child, the patient used to fear that one day she would wake up to find that her family had been taken up to Heaven, leaving her behind. The patient went to college to train as a nurse, where she fell in love with another student, who suddenly committed suicide. She believed she was responsible for him going to Purgatory, as he was an atheist and she had failed to convert him to the Faith.

Ms. X. then fell in love with another student who had applied to medical school after qualifying as a nurse. The patient went against her father's wishes and also applied to medical school but was turned down. She was devastated when she visited the medical school and discovered that her boyfriend had another girlfriend. The failure to get into medical school and the hurt caused by the failed relationship precipitated a depressive breakdown and an overdose which led to a hospital admission. The patient was treated with medication, electro-convulsive treatment and cognitive behavioural therapy.

After her discharge from hospital, Ms. X. had out-patient psychiatric support, medication and counselling over many years. The patient had had a long-standing affair with her ex-counsellor, a married man from the same church, who used to counsel her on the phone when she was upset.

She believed the world was divided into top-class people and second-rate people. Top-class people win and are successful, while second-rate people go unnoticed. The patient would often bring examples of people who were getting on with their lives in a successful way, while she was stuck in a hopeless pit of failure. As well as tormenting the patient, these ideas were also designed to goad me into greater efforts. As if she were saying, "I am second-rate and I am with a second-rate therapist, but if he did his job properly and cured me, he would become first-rate and then he would pull me up with him."

The patient believed I should stop trying to understand her and start coaching her in how to live her life. She often put me under pressure to step outside my role by suddenly announcing that she was going to do something that might adversely affect either her life or her therapy. For example, she suddenly announced that she was going to leave her permanent job and take work as an agency nurse as they were introducing a duty rota that might interfere with her attendance at therapy. The patient did not discuss her attendance at therapy with work, as she was worried it would interfere with her prospects of promotion. I immediately felt concerned that she was doing something that might damage her career and leave her feeling even less satisfied with her working life. I tried to resist the temptation to respond to my counter-transference by taking up an advisory role and instead tried to maintain an analytic response in which I interpreted the way she tried to nudge me into making advisory statements about what I thought she should or shouldn't do.

In some sessions, Ms. X. would arrive in her session and sit with her head in her hands, crying and berating herself for being useless in all areas of her life. The patient was bullied by an internal figure that was always making her feel like she was second-best. She believed the cure to this situation was to find a therapist who would demonstrate their care and devotion by breaking their usual practices. She once arrived in a session and put a scalpel on the table between us, saying that she would cut herself if I refused to help her. However, my failure to help her sufficiently led to her going to A&E complaining that she was feeling suicidal and needed to be admitted to hospital.

As much as she felt bullied, she also became the bully in her attempt to get me to change my style or demonstrate my devotion to her. The treatment offered was often measured against the "ideal" relationship provided by the previous counsellor. The abusive and corrupt nature of this relationship was ignored as she sought a "special" relationship that ignored limits and professional boundaries. The theme of special relationships is reflected in the following dream:

> Ms. X. is showing a friend her ex-counsellor's beautiful gold office. They are waiting for him to arrive, but he does not show up.

The patient feels that ordinary therapeutic understanding leaves her exposed to the problems of life's ordinary difficulties. She puts me under pressure to treat her like a special patient that breaks the bounds of ordinary, psychotherapeutic treatment. This is a re-enactment of the rapture in which a God-like figure pulls her up into Heaven, leaving ordinary human suffering and relationships below. Rosenfeld (1971) described how the borderline patient's internal world functions like a well-organised gang which defends the patient from anxieties associated with fragmentation or integration. External relationships are often recruited in ways which support this internal psychic structure. The patient's defensive organisation can remain quite stable until something in the internal or external structure breaks down. In many ways, the preference for an erotised "special" relationship with her previous therapist which had broken ethical boundaries had also caused considerable damage to my patient. It was like the glamorous dream of a golden therapeutic office with no therapy actually taking place. However, my patient understood that I rigidly kept to my boundaries in an attempt to avoid a repetition of the erotised relationship with her counsellor. She experienced this as a punitive rejection of her and her needs, rather than an attempt to provide an appropriately caring treatment situation. Ms. X. believed that being specially chosen was the only solution to her feeling second-best and she was convinced that my attempts to avoid this sort of dynamic deprived her of the treatment she needed. The desperate search for an ideal relationship overrode concerns about corruption and perverse relationships. However, on reflection, I could see that my attempts to prevent a re-enactment did leave the patient feeling uncared for and neglected. This dynamic is often the cause of inappropriate acting out by staff as they are caught up in believing they can be the patient's ideal object and resolve all their difficulties—a seduction indeed. Rey (1994) highlighted the way borderline patients search for powerful phallic solutions to repair their damaged internal worlds. Ms. X. searched for an erotised relationship with a phallic figure as an attempt to cure an underlying feeling of depression and neglect. When I did not respond to her desire to be special, keeping the professional boundary, she increased the pressure on me to tell her what to do. When this happened, she would then fit in with my expectations and hold me to account for her decisions. On one occasion, she told me that she would be missing a couple of therapy sessions because she had just bought an expensive bike and was going to compete at an elite endurance event. If she won, the event would make her feel she was a success; if she lost, it would just confirm that she was a failure. This was driven by a wish to triumph over the demands of an ordinary treatment with an ordinary therapist. The patient picked up on the disapproval in my response and withdrew her application for the race. At the following session, she accused me of suggesting that she should give up everything she enjoyed doing and slavishly commit herself to her work and therapy. She made the point that this was a betrayal, as I didn't give anything up for her, since I stuck to my discipline of trying to understand her. The patient complained that I was not available for her to contact during the weekends and evenings when she needed the most help. She made the point that she was forced to contact her ex-counsellor which left her feeling humiliated.

The patient's relationship with the therapy mirrors the world of the rapturous ascent into Heaven where she believes she will be taken up into an ideal position by a powerful God-like therapist if she devotes herself to the therapy. When I fail to promote her into a special position, she feels betrayed and gives examples of her sacrifice. Any questioning by me in the therapy of the drive to achieve the ideal state leads to a terrible fear of reprisal and punishment, just as God throws Adam and Eve out of the Garden of Eden as punishment for their disobedience.

This was a dilemma for the therapy because if the patient accepted her need for help with her difficulties, she believed she would be unloved and unlovable. This dilemma was exemplified in the following dream:

> Ms. X. was applying for a course which she believed would help her with her low self-esteem but was alarmed to discover that her curriculum vitae had a brown stain on it.

I thought the dream represented a belief that she could apply for a role as my patient in the hope of becoming her own person. However, the role of being my patient left her feeling that she had difficulties and was therefore flawed like the curriculum vitae with the brown stain. Ms. X. responded to my interpretations by saying that I had been critical of her wish to strive for the ideal. She thought I was encouraging her to accept failure since "I was just saying that she was a failure and should not strive to address her difficulties."

Ms. X.'s mind was dominated by paranoid-schizoid thinking in which she was either the ideal, with no imperfections, or else useless. There was no room in her mind for a mixed appraisal in which she might realistically accept her strengths and weaknesses. She also put pressure on me to provide ideal solutions or condemnation. Patients with EUPD often feel unloved or unlovable and seek ideal relationships with ideal objects. When the object inevitably shows evidence of human failings, this results in a blaming state of mind in which they believe that either they have failed the object or the object has failed them. The enormous pressure this puts on their relationships often results in their acrimonious breakdown. The power of the projections comes across as a concrete communication that tends to demand a concrete response. In this situation, it can be difficult to think about the underlying meaning of the transaction and communication. Segal (1981) differentiated between symbolic and concrete forms of communication. Symbolic communication conveys information about the subject's feelings and invites the listener to empathise with the emotional experience. Concrete communication has the emotional meaning squeezed out and demands, or tends to force, an action in response rather than an empathic response. Words are sometimes experienced as concrete things that have the properties of actions rather than thought. One patient told me that he did not want to talk about his murderous thoughts as he worried that they might come true. An expressed murderous feeling is undifferentiated from a murderous act.

This is complicated in the therapeutic relationship and can leave the patient and therapist at cross-purposes. While the therapist or mental health professional believes that it is important to talk about what is going on, the patient believes this is very dangerous and may lead to damage as if talking about abuse is the same as being abused.

Case example 2: The concrete nature of communication

Ms. Y. was a woman I saw for once-weekly psychotherapy. She had a diagnosis of EUPD and a long history of forming abusive relationships with men, self-harm, threats of suicide, and abusive screaming behaviour. She was convinced that all her problems would be solved if only she could escape from the flat where she had been humiliated and abused by a previous boyfriend and move into another one. She put pressure on me to write to the housing office demanding a change in her housing and became furious when I commented on her fantasy that she could leave her problems behind in the old flat. She punched the wall, leaving a dent in the plaster and screamed: "What you do not get, Mr. Evans, is that all this 'mumbo jumbo' is making me feel worse about myself. What I need is someone who is going to help me move out of that bloody flat."

In this instance, the patient feels that she is trying to get rid of memories that make her feel bad about herself. I then try to push my understanding of what she is doing back into her. This enrages her as rather than offering a home for the unmanageable aspects of herself, I am apparently forcing depressing and humiliating memories back into her. This makes her feel worse rather than better, and to her it seems I do not care. She then has to demonstrate the fact that she does not feel able to get through to me by acting out, punching the wall and screaming.

The patient puts pressure on me to relinquish my role as a therapist who offers understanding, which as she puts it, "Is about as much use as a chocolate fire guard," in preference for someone that actually does something useful, "Like a real mother." This is a common issue in the treatment of patients in borderline states of mind, as they put pressure on the therapist to provide concrete solutions. However, when the therapist does respond to concrete demands or pressures, the patient can feel that the therapist has momentarily lost their bearings or even their mind. After one of these enactments, it is common for the patient to remind the therapist that they were only exchanging ideas rather than demanding concrete action. As one very disturbed patient suddenly said to me, "You started to talk as if we needed to do something about my mind. However, that is not your role, your role is to help me think about my mind." This situation is complicated when dealing with patients in psychotic states of mind as the risk of serious acting out means that we do have to consider acting on, as well as thinking about, the symbolic meaning of actions and concrete communications.

When this happens, I think it is helpful to differentiate between the active role one might perform as a psychiatric nurse or psychiatrist and the role of a psychotherapist whose job is to understand the meaning of the patient's thoughts and behaviours (Steiner, personal communication). Sometimes, these roles can be helpfully performed by different people in a psychiatric team. However, when this is not possible, the individual therapist or mental health professional has to monitor the relationship between their role as therapist and their role as mental health professional.

Borderline patients live on the borderline between psychosis and neurosis, or put another way, they oscillate in their psychic functioning between the paranoid-schizoid and depressive positions. They often exist on the edge of the depressive position and quickly retreat into a paranoid-schizoid one at the point they experience psychic pain (Steiner, 1979). In treatment, it is sometimes possible to trace the causes of a patient's shift from the depressive to the paranoid-schizoid position, but this is usually done in hindsight.

Ms. Y. communicated her difficulties in managing any humiliating thoughts about her relationship with an abusive figure. She wanted me to support her in developing a new picture of whom she was and whom she could become. This is a view of therapy as a magical transformation that helps the patient escape from their damaged internal object relations. While I did not believe the therapy could transform her personality, I did sympathise with the patient's difficulty in facing her damaged internal world. Pushing the patient to face depressing realities before she was ready threatened to overwhelm her fragile ego with feelings of guilt and humiliation. Faced with a fragmented ego, she was then driven to seek manic solutions, employing more splitting and projection. In many ways, I had to start by helping her understand that her mind was intolerant of shortcomings and failings. The therapy could then help her moderate her internal world and develop a mind that could manage depressing realities about herself, thus reducing the reliance on primitive and manic defences.

Klein (1946) highlighted the need for the infant to internalise the primary object as a good object, which in turn forms the basis of the infant's ego. Borderline patients have often had an abusive or neglectful relationship with parental figures, so that damaged and fragile internal relationships populate their internal worlds. Borderline patients need to find supportive but boundaried figures who can help them manage their harsh internal worlds.

Case example 3: The search for a supportive relationship

A primary nurse from a psychiatric intensive care unit (PICU) presented an incident that had occurred the previous week. Ms. Z. had come to the ward under a Section of the Mental Health Act on account of her unmanageable, self-destructive behaviour. She presented herself as the victim of various abusive relationships, including with her previous psychiatric ward staff, whom she accused of maltreating her. The patient's care on the unit was divided between the nurse, who concerned herself with the patient's deliberate self-harming behaviour, and an assistant clinical psychologist who offered "abuse counselling."

During the week prior to her presentation in the supervision group, Ms. Z. had been given leave to go on a shopping trip, having reassured the nurse that she would not visit her ex-boyfriend, who was known to be violent. She was brought back by the police the next day, having been severely assaulted by her ex-boyfriend. The nurse described how she had to sit in on the clinical examination with the patient while the doctor examined her beaten body. She described the patient's cold, cut-off, and matter-of-fact way of presenting herself for examination after the physical assault. She commented on how detached the patient seemed from her body and from the events that led up to her being so badly beaten. The nurse was visibly shaken by this experience and finished by saying she was disgusted by the damage done and did not know if she was cut out for this type of work.

In the group discussion, several problems with Ms. Z.'s management emerged. Her self-destructive behaviour had encouraged previous institutions to take responsibility for keeping her alive by putting her on continual close observations along with detention under the Mental Health Act. This became an unhelpful, malignant pattern whereby she projected all responsibility for her well-being into the staff. When the patient was admitted to the current unit, they had hoped to reverse the trend by encouraging her to act in a more adult-like and responsible way. She had given the impression of being insightful, articulate, and motivated to co-operate with the plan.

Taken off her Section as a result of her apparent progress, Ms. Z. was in preparation for discharge at the time of the assault. The assistant clinical psychologist thought the therapeutic work had been going very well and described the patient as a likeable woman, who showed tremendous potential as an artist. The primary nurse felt more reticent about the patient's progress and mentioned that the deliberate self-harming behaviour had continued on a regular and increasingly frequent basis. She felt that she was more fragile than she was presenting to the assistant psychologist and had worried that her self-harm would increase as the discharge plan was implemented.

Ms. Z.'s improvement was sustainable as long as the ward staff continued to care for her. The moment they decided to plan a discharge, the destructive aspects of her personality, located in the acting-out behaviour, increased in regularity and violence. As well as punishing the ward, her actions can be seen as an attempt to show staff that she needed to feel they understood the level of her difficulties. The patient had very little capacity for tolerating frustration or metabolising her psychological state. She used action to evacuate undigested psychological experience. In the example above, different parts of the patient were communicated to different parts of the team. The assistant clinical psychologist was in touch with the patient's abilities and resources, while the nurse was more in tune with the underlying fragility and damage.

Ms. Z. presented herself as a victim of historically abusive relationships. The clinical team's approach was based on an idea that they needed to support the patient in separating from these abusive external figures. This approach denied the patient's ongoing unconscious involvement with abusive internal figures and the way these internal relationships became re-enacted in the transference with staff. The meaning of the patient's acting out was ignored in an attempt to avoid malignant cycles of care. However, the acting out indicated a serious problem in the patient's relationship with herself and her internal objects. In many ways, they are a message that says, "I may look OK on the outside, but I'm damaged inside." In his paper "On Arrogance," Bion (1958) describes a group of "borderline psychotic" patients who experienced a catastrophic breakdown in their maternal relationship as infants. The breakdown of this relationship leads to a deficit in the ego, as the infant fails to internalise the mother as a good object, who is able to help him or her digest emotional experience. The infant internalises an "ego destructive superego" instead of an internal good object. This kind of superego demands ideals in the infant's self and their objects. On further discussion, it emerged that Ms. Z. had a voice in her head that demanded she harm herself whenever she experienced anxiety or concern about her future. She hated the dependent aspects of herself which exposed her to knowing about her feelings of vulnerability and need. These experiences were then projected into her body and attacked by a highly critical internal figure, who acted as if anxieties or vulnerabilities could be burnt or cut out. The visit to the abusive ex-boyfriend externalised this internal dynamic, as he attacked her and treated her in an abusive and hostile way.

This action shifts the attention from the patient's internal relationship with a bullying figure that attacks her, to an external relationship with the abusive man. The patient's apparent co-operation with the planned discharge does not consider her anxieties about being left on her own with her abusive internal voices. Anxiety about her ability to cope without the ward's support is expressed through the acting out. This forces the team to look at the extent of the patient's damaged relationship with herself, expressed through her beaten body. It is interesting to note that the nurse is sickened by the sight of the patient's damaged body, but to a degree that prevents her from being able to think about the seriousness of this abusive internal relationship. Patients with borderline features often describe a part of the self that passively looks on while they abuse themselves or allow themselves to be abused. One patient said that she watched herself attack herself through cutting but felt powerless to stop it. The observing self of Ms. Z.'s non-psychotic mind is projected into the nurse who must look on her battered body, feeling sickened and helpless, unable to prevent the harm done. Britton built on Bion's ideas in a 1989 paper titled "The Missing Link." In this paper, he describes the way patients deal with a breakdown in the mother-infant relationship. The infant splits off and projects the mother's unavailability, creating an illusion of an ideal relationship, which they cling to and control. Any separation or breakdown in understanding between the infant and the mother is projected outward into the father, who is now experienced as a threatening, disruptive presence. Borderline patients try to establish an ideal relationship with an ideally supportive object. In the initial stages, any break in the ideal situation can be split off and denied. But when things reach a critical point, there is an explosion of acting out or verbal outburst. The ward's planning for her discharge left Ms. Z. to deal with her adverse internal and external relationships without the support of the nursing team. She tried to maintain an ideal relationship with the unit by denying her anxieties and feelings about discharge. These were projected into her body, and then when they reach a particular pitch, she acts out by visiting her ex-boyfriend, who is known to be violent. This externalises the internal conflict, so that he is the one that attacks her body, rather than her ego-destructive superego. The body, which carries the evidence of her hatred for the part of her that depended on the unit for care and attention, is attacked. While the patient remains detached and uninvolved in the examination of her body, the nurse is filled with horror at the extent of the damage (Evans, 2016). Borderline patients need help in separating from the influence of tyrannical, internal figures that tend to dominate their internal world. Ms. Z. found it hard to acknowledge the degree of her dependence upon staff to help her with feelings of self-hatred and loathing. Her actions communicated anxiety about being left on her own with a tyrannical internal figure that attacked her for any perceived weakness or failing. She visits the ex-boyfriend to be beaten by him so that her internal and external scenarios will match. Why? Because there is relief from her psychic conflict when it is externalised.

Case example 4: Separation from a tyrannical internal figure

Mr. A.B. was a man in his late 20s who came into therapy in a crisis and suffering from what he called depression. He was sexually promiscuous and led a manic lifestyle, throwing himself into different relationships. These would often end in him feeling mistreated, rejected, and suicidal. The patient's father had died at an early age and he had been brought up by his mother. The patient returned home to visit his mother most weekends, despite describing her as being critical and disapproving of him. This intensely critical relationship was repeated in the treatment where I felt under intense critical scrutiny.

Mr. A.B.'s mother would often become the voice for this harsh and critical internal object, as he would quote her saying what a disappointment he was. He told me how he often thought he would fall onto the railway tracks on the way to sessions and lose the use of his legs. This represented a reprisal by his tyrannical superego that could not stand any admission of weakness or dependence upon help. The patient felt that attending therapy and getting help in thinking about the severity of his internal world exposed him to retaliation from this possessive and murderous internal figure. Indeed, he feared that this murderous figure would rather push him onto the train tracks than be exposed in therapy sessions.

At other times, Mr. A.B.'s internal world changed as he moved from being the victim of a murderous superego to becoming a tyrannical figure himself. Any shortcomings of mine in terms of understanding or emotional attunement were immediately pointed out in a highly critical way. Moreover, I often had the feeling of being on a knife edge, as the patient wanted attention to his mental disorder but any phrase or comment that made him feel upset could produce a violent, verbal response. If he felt that I did not take my responsibilities for his condition seriously, he would increase the volume and veracity of the complaint, with the desire of getting through to me.

The tyrannical superego demands that the ego evacuate anything that causes psychological pain or conflict. Bion described patients like this as developing minds that act like a muscle to project psychic problems into the external world rather than digest them. Mr. A.B. would push a serious problem into me, but if I tried to talk with him about the problem, he responded by saying that he was bored with that issue and wanted to move on and talk about something else.

Rey (1994) used to say that these patients lacked an internal spine and had no clear identity. He thought that they were looking for a "marsupial pouch" into which they could project a part of their internal world. They project so powerfully and so concretely that the interactions often have a profound effect upon the therapist's mind. Consequently, their projections are often accompanied by a fear that the therapist will retaliate by pushing the projection back into them.

Having projected unwanted aspects of themselves, they then want to control the object, as they fear losing touch with the aspects of themselves that have been projected into the object. Rey (1994) described the claustro-agoraphobic dilemma intrinsic to borderline patients' relationships with their object. If they are too close they fear being overwhelmed, but if the object is too far away, they fear feeling detached from a precious aspect of themselves. This concept is also known as the *core complex* and is discussed in relation to suicidality in Chapter 5. Hence Mr. A.B. would often get into a panic approaching breaks fearing that I would die. He then feared being overwhelmed by all of the aspects of himself that had been projected into me for safe-keeping. Borderline patients often use their eyes to control the object and in the case of Mr. A.B., I had the experience of being watched like a hawk and my reactions and responses carefully monitored. He was always worried that I would be driven to act out or do something unpredictable as a result of the amount of unmanageable, unwanted psychic debris he projected into me. If I moved around or looked uncomfortable, he worried that I was being made ill by his demands.

In the scenario described above, the therapist is involved in an intense transference relationship requiring absolute emotional attunement. Pressure is put on the therapist to act as an ideal figure and any separation between patient and therapist causes violent emotional storms. It is as if the therapist becomes the failed mother that has dropped the infant in favour of their relationship with the father. The infant then nags, cajoles, and criticises the mother into leaving the father and turning her attention back to the infant. This can become part of a grievance against the mother for failing to provide ideal and continuous care. Any separation is attacked as an impediment to the ideal relationship the infant relies on to survive.

In his paper "Subjectivity and Objectivity," Britton (2004) describes the patient's difficulty in bringing together his/her subjective self with an objective view. Borderline patients fear the integration of subjective experience with objective thought as this heralds painful realisations about reality that interfere with their psychic equilibrium. Patients in borderline states of mind are sensitive to any communication that contains an objective assessment of the patient's behaviour, as this is felt to threaten the patient's subjective experience. Mr. A.B. once said, "If you say that I want you to be an ideal therapist one more time I am going to hit you. I feel like you are saying you are not the right therapist for me and you're trying to get me to go to someone else." In this instance, the patient felt I was trying to get away from him by suggesting I could not fit in with his demand to be the ideal. He attacks me by threatening to hit me in an attempt to get me to behave in an ideal way. Joseph (1985) describes how patients behave in ways which nudge the analyst into behaviour which fits with their expectations and defensive needs. On many occasions, he said that I was banned from talking about separation, as if we could live in a bubble which excluded the reality of loss. However, if I was influenced by these threats and failed to pre-empt the significance of breaks or separations, it would precipitate some dramatic acting out, as the reality suddenly hit him in a very traumatic way.

Mr. A.B. was highly sensitive to my tone of voice which he believed expressed whether I was engaged or not, and he would often ask me whether I was bored or tired. He hated intellectual comments and would say that he had wasted his time coming if I could not be empathic or authentic. In these situations, I had to take in his perception of me. If I said anything that contradicted his perception, he would become more insistent saying that I was accusing him of lying and threatened to throw a brick through the window of the building with a note attached saying what "A fucking jobsworth I was." The patient was also sensitive to any interpretation or comment that lacked authenticity, or a feeling of my being unengaged. Again, if he felt I was pushing the problem back into him or failing to take his perception seriously, he would threaten to contact the complaints department and lodge a complaint. If we had an unsatisfactory session, he would phone the secretary's office to leave a message saying I had left him with suicidal feelings. The patient sometimes collapsed into states of self-hatred and self-loathing. If he picked up anything slightly judgemental in my comments, he would accuse me of pushing my responsibilities back onto him. He would respond by saying he did not think Nazis were allowed to train as therapists.

Technical challenges

This brings us on to some of the technical problems of treating patients with a diagnosis of EUPD. First, we have to listen to what they are saying and try to get on their wavelength. The most helpful way of thinking about the patient's clinical material is that in some way they are always trying to tell us something and we have to understand where they are coming from. Borderline patients are persecuted by the ideal, what they should have or would like to have been. This dynamic gets re-enacted in the relationship with the therapist.

> Mr. A.B. once told me that he had spent the weekend with his mother who spoke the whole time about how marvellously his cousin was doing with his new child. She then said to the patient that she had given up waiting for him to produce grandchildren as he was hopeless with women. The patient drew breath then said to me, "Are you bored? Why aren't you saying anything? Perhaps you agree with her that I'm a waste of time."

We can see here how the breakdown in the relationship between the patient and his object is repeated in the therapy. The patient tells me a problem and when I don't immediately reply, he feels I am disinterested and that I feel he is a waste of time and so I am unavailable. In this way, I become like the object that won't take anything in about his state of mind. Another patient used to open the door, sit down in the chair and say aggressively, "Oh thanks very much! I come all this way and you can't even be bothered to say hello." The strength of the accusation can provoke either an apologetic or a defensive response in the therapist. This has an effect on the therapist's ability to maintain an analytic stance. Thus, professionals can get into a cycle of acting out with the patient. With Mr. A.B. the moment he says that he lives in a very cruel world, meaning his internal world, he starts to cry. Then the next second he retreats into a position of mocking himself.

"Oh, I hate this wingeing 'oh poor me.'" In this state, he descends into self-hatred and mockery.

In my experience, it helps to take the complaints seriously and try to always see things from the patient's point of view in the first instance, with the assumption that they are trying to tell us something. This can be very difficult, especially when you feel that their view of you is grossly unfair, but it does not help to push it back into the patient as this is responding defensively, rather than analytically. It does help to consider what it is they are saying. Steiner (1993) outlined the difference between what he described as "analyst-centred" and "patient-centred interpretations." The analyst-centred interpretation involves taking a view of how the patient views the analyst, while the patient-centred interpretation focuses on the patient.

Patients who lack a good internal object need to feel that the external object understands their feelings. They need to feel they are with a therapist who can take in the patient's view of the therapist. They also need to feel they are with someone who is empathic and in sympathy with their situation. The counter-transference is unconscious and we are prone to respond, without being fully aware of our motives. Borderline patients are extremely sensitive to the therapist's tone of voice and use of language. These patients pick up on any hint of criticism in your tone of voice or lack of warmth. The problem is that some patients are tyrannical in their control and provoke the therapist into a defensive position. These patients are very sensitive to this and tend to react badly as they easily feel that they are being given cold charity or patronised. As one patient used to say, "You are as engaged as a wall." This is a technical problem with borderline patients as any hint of feedback that has not been digested and thought through is experienced as an assault. This sort of response can lead to a rapid deterioration in their mental state, as the patient tries to force the message home by escalating the strength of their communication and by acting out.

Discussion

Borderline patients live on a mental knife edge as their perception of themselves oscillates between ideas of triumphant success and catastrophic failure. The ego-destructive superego governs this state of mind. Lucas (2009) thought the process of therapy was to provide support and help build a perspective so the patient's ego can separate from the influence of the superego. Thus, the therapist's objective is to turn the patient's ego from balancing on a knife edge to something a little wider—a gymnastics bar would be an improvement!

Many patients come into therapy or treatment expecting to be restored to an ideal state, and they put pressure on the therapist to act as an omnipotent God who can remove all their problems. Ms. X. (see case example 1 in this chapter) believed she had an ideal relationship with her previous counsellor who demonstrated his devotion by breaking his ethical boundaries and developing a corrupt relationship with her.

This is an example of a difference in the expectations between the therapist and the patient. Whereas I took the view that the relationship with the "ideal" interfered with her development and capacity to engage with life, the patient believed this relationship would save her life. The difference in expectations between the therapist and the patient can lead to conflict and a sense of frustration. The patient believes the therapy will restore them to an ideal state, while the therapist is trying to help the patient come to terms with their normal imperfections and difficulties. Pressure is applied through the counter-transference on the therapist to provide omnipotent solutions. The patient fears that the extent of their difficulties cannot be solved by ordinary means and hence they seek magical solutions. However, when a patient senses the therapist is being omnipotent in response to the pressure, he/she may also become wary, feeling that the therapist has become corrupt or lost their mind.

The counter-transference provides valuable information about the patient's state of mind. Borderline patients have difficulties dealing with the psychic contents of their minds and tend to evacuate undigested elements of their minds through action. They also put considerable pressure on mental health practitioners to act, rather than think. Ideally, the function of the mental health practitioner with these patients is to use their verbal capacity to reverse the process and turn the action, and pressure towards action, back into words. However, if mental health professionals or therapists prematurely push insight back to the patient or rush the patient's development, it can cause a rapid fragmentation. Progress is often dependent upon supportive relationships even if the patient plays down the significance of these relationships. Borderline patients do not like being reminded of their underlying fragility and dependence upon others—yet hate it to be forgotten.

In some ways it is helpful to think of a therapeutic relationship as having two elements: a caring element and a treatment element. Steiner (1993) describes two phases of analytic work. In the first phase, the therapist takes in the patient's view of things and tries to understand how they see things. In the second phase, the therapist has to separate themselves from the patient's view and come to their own understanding of the patient and their problems. This involves a process of being affected by the patient and their perceptions and then separating to develop an objective view.

Conclusion

Borderline patients rely on relationships with people who understand them to give them support to manage their damaged internal world. However, the second stage of the therapeutic process can easily overwhelm the patient with feelings of guilt about the damage done, which leads to fragmentation. The patient needs to feel that the therapist cares about them and their lives. Patients get anxious if they feel that they are with a therapist who is emotionally cut off, or oblivious to their suffering. In many ways, the patient requires the therapist to combine objective thought with empathy. You could say that these patients need to feel that they are being cared for by someone that contains a parental couple that can come together to treat and care for a troubled infant. Helping the therapist maintain their internal couple will depend on many things, including an opportunity to discuss the inevitable obstacles that arise in treatment. Understanding these obstacles to development can deepen the therapist's clinical understanding of the patient and their difficulties and allow the therapist to support the patient, while helping them integrate projected aspects of themselves. This in turn helps the patient reduce their reliability on violent projection as a means of dealing with psychic pain.

References

Bion, W. R. (1958). On arrogance. *International Journal of Psychoanalysis, 39*(5), 341–346.

Britton, R. (1989a). *Belief and imagination*. London & New York, NY: Routledge.

Britton, R. (1989b). The missing link: Parental sexuality in the Oedipus complex. In R. Britton, M. Feldman & E. O'Shaughnessy (Eds.), *The Oedipus complex today: Clinical implications* (pp. 83–101). London: Karnac Books.

Britton, R. (2004). Subjectivity, objectivity, and triangular space. *The Psychoanalytic Quarterly, 73*(1), 47–61. DOI: 10.1002/j.2167-4086.2004.tb00152.x.

Evans, M. J. (2016). Being driven mad: Towards understanding borderline states. In M. Wadell and J. Catty (Eds.), *Making room for madness in mental health: The psychoanalytic understanding of psychotic communication* (pp. 61–85). London: Karnac Books.

Joseph, B. (Ed.). (1985). Transference: The total situation. *International Journal of Psychoanalysis, 66*, 447–454. Republished in E. Spillius (ed.) *Melanie Klein today*, Vol. 2. Routledge (1988).

Klein, M. (1935). A contribution to the psychogenesis of manic-depressive states. *International Journal of Psychoanalysis, 16*, 145–174.

Klein, M. (1940). Mourning and its relation to manic depressive states. *International Journal of Psychoanalysis, 21*, 125–153.

Klein, M. (1946). Notes on some schizoid mechanisms. *International Journal of Psychoanalysis, 27*(3–4), 99–110.

Lucas, R. (2009). Differentiating psychotic processes from psychotic disorders. In D. Birksted-Breen (Ed.), *The psychotic wavelength: A psychoanalytic perspective for psychiatry*. London: Routledge.

Rey, H. (1994). *Universals of psychoanalysis in the treatment of psychotic and borderline states*. London: Free Association Books.

Rosenfeld, H. (1971). A clinical approach to the psychoanalytic theory of the life and the death instincts: An investigation of the aggressive aspects of narcissism. *International Journal of Psychoanalysis, 52*(2), 169–178.

Segal, H. (1981). Notes on symbol formation. In *The works of Hanna Segal, A Kleinian approach to clinical practice*. New York, NY: Jason Aronson.

Steiner, J. (1979). The border between the paranoid-schizoid position and depressive positions in the borderline patient. *British Journal of Medical Psychology, 52*(4), 385–391.

Steiner, J. (1993). Problems of psychoanalytic technique: Patient-centred and analyst-centred interpretations. In *Psychic retreats: Pathological organisations of the personality in psychotic, neurotic, and borderline patients* (pp. 116–130). London: Routledge.

Chapter 7

Tuning in to psychotic communication on a psychiatric intensive care unit

Following the closure of the large mental hospitals in the 1980s, we now find that only the most disturbed patients (usually under a Section of the Mental Health Act) are admitted to hospital. Pressure on beds means that patients are often discharged as soon as there is a reduction in risk, and for psychotic patients, this is often linked to a reduction in their positive symptoms. This deprives the patient of an opportunity to consolidate their improved mental state and also deprives ward staff of their job satisfaction in seeing their patients improve.

This results in staff coping with high numbers of patients who often act out their difficulties in violent ways, driven by impulsive or psychotic states of mind. An international review of assaults on staff working in psychiatric settings (Staff Victims of Psychiatric Patient Assaults Review of Public Findings 2013–2017) commented on the high level of physical and verbal assaults and sexual harassment experienced by staff in these settings. Nursing staff are particularly vulnerable to attack, which often leads to sick leave or absence from work and high staff turnover.

I will use my observations in providing psychoanalytic supervision on various acute psychiatric admission wards and intensive care units to illustrate my ideas about the treatment and care of psychotic patients. Through case discussion, this kind of supervision aims to deepen the staff team's understanding of a particular patient and the difficulties they present. Attention is paid to the relationship between the patient's history, their internal world, and the means of communication they are employing. A psychoanalytic model is particularly helpful when thinking about psychotic or borderline functioning. It can help restore the missing emotional meaning to moments of acting out and concrete communication by psychotic minds so that clinicians can remain interested in their patients' emotional life. This matters because staff are then prepared to listen out for moments of meaning, even where the predominant or prevailing discourse seems to be driven by concrete action.

When the violent actions or verbal assaults by a patient are brought to the supervision setting, the patient's emotional dilemmas can begin to be understood in the counter-transference. Admission to the "bricks and mortar" of a hospital setting is a unique opportunity for a patient to have their unmanageable psychic state understood, and therefore contained.

In these sessions, staff find valuable psychological space to separate from the effects of the patient's projections and their concrete actions and think about them symbolically. By concentrating on the transference and counter-transference, staff are encouraged to take an interest in their patient's histories, their delusional systems, and patterns of behaviour. The patient's actions on the ward, which are often repeated patterns of behaviour, as well as their relationships with staff, are both examined. It is important for staff teams to keep an open mind about the nature of the patient's difficulties, gathering information from different sources to establish a dynamic picture of the forces that drive the patient's thinking and behaviour. Deepening their understanding of the patient helps to increase the therapeutic potential of the patient's admission and to motivate the staff on the unit to stay engaged and enriched by their work with these challenging and difficult-to-nurse patients.

Case example 1: Breakdown in symbolic thinking

Mr. C.D. was referred to the ward after a serious assault in which he broke a member of staff's jaw. His mood and behaviour were described as fluctuating between relatively calm and highly unpredictable. However, he remained paranoid towards patients and staff, believing they were coughing in his food during meal times. Male members of the nursing team described a repeated pattern of behaviour where, without warning, he would punch the male member of staff he was talking to, saying he was not gay and that they had no right to touch him. On other occasions, he would suddenly declare that it was all right for them to talk because the member of staff was really female.

In contrast, female members of the team reported that he would be talking to them and then suddenly touch them as if they were his sexual partner. Staff said that these changes in behaviour happened very suddenly—out of the blue—and in response to moments when they felt they might have made some emotional contact with the patient. The patient had a delusional belief that he was "alpha male" and that he was a private investigator.

I thought Mr. C.D.'s capacity to maintain a difference between symbolic and concrete thinking had broken down as he became threatened by feelings of vulnerability and dependency.

In a paper called "Unprovoked Assaults," Sohn (1997) describes the way a man projected unwanted aspects of himself into a stranger whom he then attacked. Thus, the projection of his damaged self is accompanied by a physical action that concretely locates the damage in the other man. I thought Mr. C.D. identified himself as a heterosexual, alpha male, lone wolf, phallic figure who does not need anyone but locates desires in those around him. Once these desires have been projected into the male member of staff, their interest, warmth, and curiosity are experienced as a homosexual seduction and Mr. C.D. lashes out to protect his threatened heterosexual identity. Alternatively, with female members of staff, desire for contact and care is projected into them and sexualised. He then believes that they are attracted to him as a phallic figure whom they are trying to excite. At other times, he suddenly announces that it is all right for him to talk to a male member of staff because the male member of staff is a woman, thus avoiding the need to assault him.

Bronstein (2018) notes the way delusional systems can be used to protect the object from assault. Mr. C.D's solution is to assault the reality of the member of staff's sexual identity rather than actually assault them. In this state of mind, the relationship with external reality is treated like a malleable cartoon that can be changed according to the patients' needs and wishes.

I thought the delusion of Mr. C.D. being a private investigator was connected with the need for a part of himself to arrest the violent and predatory alpha-male self. Indeed, the private investigator might discover that this powerful phallic fantasy was masking the reality of an infantile figure that needed care and attention. His phantasy of being an alpha male allows him to feel he is a powerfully seductive, phallic figure that women cannot resist. This defends him from the reality of being a patient on a PICU, dependent upon staff for care and attention. I thought the phantasy that people were coughing into his food represented the threat posed by sanity. As if sane people would contaminate his made-up world of self-sufficiency and power with which he feeds himself.

In the supervision group discussion, we talked about the need to pay attention to the patient's need for care and attention while understanding that this can quickly turn into a threatening situation, if he feels his passive desires for care threaten his masculine identity. He is then likely to deal with this threat by becoming the active phallic male, who either seduces the women or assaults the men. Staff reported back that this approach seemed to lead to a reduction in the number of assaults.

Case example 2: Assault on sanity

Mr. E.F. was admitted and treated under a Section of the Mental Health Act after his sister contacted psychiatric services to say that he had relapsed. The patient had been admitted on numerous occasions over many years. He had a persistent belief that he was the Prime Minister of England and would return to 10 Downing Street once it had been cleared of bubonic plague. At other times, he believed he was a detective or a billionaire who was going to build a canteen for staff. He also suffered night-time hallucinations of being cut up or having his internal organs eaten by worms.

After being admitted to the hospital, Mr. E.F. was frequently transferred to the Psychiatric Intensive Care Unit as a result of his assaults on staff. For example, he physically attacked staff as they administered his anti-psychotic medication by intra-muscular depot, convinced that they were trying to infect him with bubonic plague. He had a spell of goose-stepping up and down the ward claiming he was

Mussolini and screaming racist abuse at black staff. On another occasion, he violently assaulted his sister for visiting him on the ward, after he "had disowned her" from being a part of his family. It is important to note that patients in disturbed states of mind usually calm down when they find themselves in a clinical setting that offers an appropriate level of containment. The PICU is a locked ward with a relatively high staff-to-patient ratio, but this improvement did not happen with the patient, who remained verbally aggressive and highly grandiose.

So, we can surmise that in the acute stages of this illness, Mr. E.F. attacked any version of reality that interfered with his delusional system fanatically and violently. He intimidated staff in order to control their version of reality—his identification with Mussolini related to a dictatorial state of mind that projected vulnerability and other unwanted aspects of his mind into other patients', whom he described as being mad, while members of staff were racially abused. He became intimidating when anyone dared to challenge his grandiose and dictatorial state of mind. The fear of contamination from bubonic plague was related to his fear of having his manic, delusional world undermined or infected by reality. His behaviour is driven by a tyrannical state of mind dominated by his psychotic belief in the authority of his position. In this state of mind, his victim is dehumanised into being someone that is interfering with his way of thinking and therefore deserves to be attacked.

He was treated with a high-dose, anti-psychotic depot medication, refusing all oral treatments. This subdued the violence but not the other symptoms. Even then, Mr. E.F. refused to leave the ward as he believed he would be assassinated. After some time, these anxieties reduced and staff were able to escort the patient on leave. Over time, this work seemed to lead to a change in the clinical presentation, in that he was more able to manage relationships with staff and patients. The occupational therapist (OT) mentioned that he had joined in activities without causing problems and made valuable contributions to the group activities.

Patients in the acute phase of a psychotic illness project their sane awareness of their illness into others while immersing themselves in their psychosis. In the case of Mr. E.F., this is a tyrannical state of mind represented by his identification with Mussolini, whom he imagines lived a doubt-free existence. His sister represents sanity by contacting psychiatric services. As Mr. E.F.'s condition improves, his sanity and awareness of reality fluctuates with delusional thinking. This provokes depressive states of mind and the patient may return to his psychosis in an attempt to avoid a depressive collapse or fragmentation of the ego. The nihilistic delusions of being eaten by worms in his night terrors reveal the patient's underlying savage melancholia which could lead to a suicidal state. It is important to remember that patients who suffer from a psychotic condition are at the highest risk of suicide when either losing their minds or coming out of psychosis.

The term "double bookkeeping" has been used to describe a state in which the patient accepts treatment while denying he has an illness (Bortolotti, 2011). As Mr. E.F. calmed down, he became more compliant with treatment and enjoyed the care and attention of the ward even while denying his need for treatment. There is a danger that acknowledging his illness and dependence upon the hospital for treatment and care would threaten his ego with depressive collapse. It is common for patients with psychotic conditions to develop post-traumatic depression when their insight grows into the extent of their condition. When a patient's ego is fragile, this work can threaten to overwhelm the ego and lead to the re-emergence of paranoid-schizoid defences, as the patient splits off and projects different parts of the ego.

Rosenfeld (1971) developed the idea of a defensive structure that acted like an internal gang and offered protection from psychic pain, in return for loyalty. Any move by healthy aspects of the patient towards help may be undermined and attacked by destructive aspects of their internal world. Although healthy elements of the patient may consciously wish to divorce themselves from the gang's influence, the person is often unconsciously dependent upon the gang in subtle ways. The healthy part of the patient needs help and support in its struggle with the internal gang and its attempt to form healthy relationships with good and helpful figures in the external world. I believe it is the staff team's persistence in working with Mr. E.F., combined with the preceding influence of the anti-psychotic medication, which helped reduce his reliance on psychotic defences and thus ameliorate the psychotic anxieties. Although patients often prefer their mania to sanity, they also fear getting trapped inside their psychosis as it leads to a neglect of external reality. I thought the reference to himself as a detective referred to a sane part that was trying to identify and apprehend the psychotic part of his personality that seemed to be "getting away with murder." Thus, we can see the dynamic interplay represented by a psychotic and non-psychotic part of his personality.

In the case of Mr. E.F., problems arose after his discharge, as the psychotic narcissistic structure that offered pain-free solutions based on a denial of dependency, came back into the ascendancy. Without the support of the PICU and the sense of reality represented by the staff, he is pulled back into a grandiose, delusional world in which he is a God-like figure that does not need to take account of ordinary realities like accommodation, hygiene, and clothing. The underlying depressive mood is evident to onlookers because he looks like a homeless person, while he lives in a world of his grandiose creation. Psychotic patients need services to take a long-term view of their difficulties as they move through different stages of their condition.

Case example 3: The delusion as a defence against depressive breakdown and fragmentation

Mr. G.H. had been detained in a high-secure forensic hospital for many years after being found guilty of murdering a woman. He was arrested in the park next to the woman's body after stabbing her many times. The police said he made no attempt to resist arrest but presented in a bizarre way. His language was broken up and they couldn't make any sense of his communication apart from the fact that he seemed elated. After several days in custody, his behaviour changed from the bizarre and chaotic state into a cut-off, controlled state of mind. On questioning several days later, Mr. G.H. said that he was king of a planet on the edge of the galaxy called Sapson and that his spaceship had crashed on his way to another planet. When asked what he was doing in a high-secure hospital, he replied that he was waiting for his spaceship to be repaired so that he could continue with his mission.

We can see how this delusion protects Mr. G.H. from the guilt of acknowledging his crime or the reality of his psychiatric breakdown. The content of his delusional system is manic and grandiose, as the patient has crowned himself King of Sapson, thus casting himself as an important person on a life-saving mission. This allows him to deny the reality of the fact that he was being detained in a high-secure hospital for having *taken* the life of a woman. As King of Sapson, Mr. G.H. was protected from feelings of inadequacy and rage about being small, or insignificant. It is not too hard to imagine that such emotions might well have been the kinds of feelings that caused him to murder in the first place, just at the point when his mind's capacity to function was breaking down. The underlying depressive content was represented by the fact that Sapson was on the edge of the galaxy, very, very far away from the sun, and so he was consequently cold, depressed, and lifeless.

The delusion therefore offers protection for the patient from persecutory anxieties, since, first, it creates a world free from guilt. After all, the King of Sapson is on a mission to save his planet from collapse and destruction *in the future*. Whereas the painful reality is that the destruction of his mind in the form of a breakdown has already happened. Secondly, the delusion also protects Mr. G.H. from this depressing realisation. Thus the delusion acts as a rigid, concrete container that protects Mr. G.H. from anxieties about fragmentation or depressive collapse. However, it is at the expense of reality testing and personal growth.

The patient reminded me of some of the patients I nursed on the long-stay wards of Springfield Hospital, in the early 1980s, while training as a psychiatric nurse. These patients spent very little time engaging with anyone outside their own mind as they mainly lived in their delusional worlds. I saw how they led emotionally impoverished lives as they had withdrawn from the world of shared reality. However, even the most deluded patients had some awareness of external reality as they all queued in an orderly fashion at the same time every day for food and cigarettes.

Case example 4: The in-patient unit as a container that helps the patient bear psychic pain

Mr. I.J. contacted the police saying he needed to be deported as he had murdered someone. On investigation, no evidence of murder was found. Indeed, after the interview, the police referred him to a psychiatric team for examination. At the assessment he presented in an aggressive, provocative manner, and the team found no evidence of mental illness and discharged him. Several days after this assessment, the patient was arrested for assaulting a police officer who had been called by a shopkeeper, because he was attempting to steal goods. It subsequently emerged that he had also assaulted his uncle several days earlier. He was remanded in prison where he claimed that he had been sent by Muhammed to teach his uncle a lesson because he had not given him "the Power." After examination by the in-reach psychiatrist, it was agreed to transfer him to a psychiatric hospital for assessment and treatment. He was admitted to the Psychiatric Intensive Care Unit.

During the week on the ward, Mr. I.J. remained mute and appeared to be paranoid and suspicious. The ward OT and other staff worked hard to engage him and he gradually started a more open style of communication, revealing what appeared to be delusional thinking. Anti-psychotic medication was commenced and after a few weeks, the clinical picture started to change. Staff reported that he was acting in a superior and grandiose way, standing in front of the television and hogging the remote control. When challenged about this behaviour by nursing staff, he became abusive and very threatening towards them, threatening to cut them up into little bits with a knife. There were also chilling threats towards staff during this time. These verbal assaults were escalating to physically assaultive behaviour, and consequently, he was nursed in seclusion. While in seclusion, staff continued to take an interest in the patient despite his abusive and threatening attitude. The clinical presentation was unclear and, rather than being psychotic, the patient presented in an anti-social way, suggesting he would not respond to treatment and the view of some members of the staff team was that he should return to prison and face trial for his assaults on his uncle and the police officer. However, the consultant, the OT, and some members of the nursing team thought it was possible that a psychotic process was driving the threatening, anti-social behaviour. In particular, the ward OT had made an effort to contact the prison and find out details of his presentation during his detainment and the history of his arrest.

During his time in prison, Mr. I.J. was reported as being in the full grip of his psychosis as he talked openly about his delusional beliefs without any concern about what others might think. Indeed, he fervently attempted to convert others to his way of thinking. However, once admitted to the psychiatric hospital, his state of mind shifts into one of wariness and suspicion and he withdraws into a mute state. This shift may have been assisted by the influence of the anti-psychotic medication or the fact of his admission to a psychiatric unit. I would argue that the patient's guarded state of mind is driven by the psychotic part of his personality which wants to conceal his psychosis. Then, when the paranoia subsides, it is replaced by the aggressive "gangster" who sees himself as dominating the ward. This transformation involves a shift from a psychotic belief that he is the "all knowing" messenger to an apparent personality-disordered state of being the "all powerful" gangster.

As well as providing a mask for the psychosis, one can also see the influence of the psychosis in his personality-disordered presentation. These different states of mind are all used as an attempt to cure his underlying feelings of depression and worthlessness. The depressed state of mind is evident when he feels he has been deprived of his power to control his environment (i.e. sent to seclusion), when he tells the police he needed to be deported or when he demands he should be sent back to prison for punishment. Provoking hatred in others also satisfies a melancholic wish for punishment and rejection.

As the episodes of aggression continued, anti-psychotic medication was restarted, which at times he refused, so he was consequently forcibly medicated. Following a series of supervisions in which we discussed Mr. I.J., the ward staff resisted the temptation provoked by the patient to send him back to prison and it was evident over time that he responded to the anti-psychotic medication and the interest shown in him by the staff team. As he revealed more about the nature of his thinking, the team learned that he had been separated from his mother and brought to this country by his uncle at an early age. Initially, he and his uncle had lived with an aunt and uncle. He did well at school and sport but was disappointed to discover that he could not represent a club athletics team, on account of the fact that his uncle had failed to register him as a British citizen. Time passed, and he started to give up on his studies and drifted into a life of gangs and criminal activity. Eventually, the aunt asked him and his uncle to leave her house.

It is common for patients who become aware of despairing feelings about their damaged self to turn to a God-like figure in their delusions who can provide magical solutions. We could surmise that Mr. I.J. harboured a grievance towards his uncle for failing to provide him with a psychological "home"—i.e. to provide him with an identity citizenship and a mind that could manage his feelings of humiliation and worthlessness. The grandiose delusion that he was a powerful messenger from God provides an illusory cure for his abiding feelings of impotence, depression, and worthlessness. All weakness and feelings of failure about himself are projected into the uncle, who is then attacked and punished for being so weak. By reporting a murder to the police and telling them he should be deported, he gave a warning of what was about to happen. In this psychotic state of mind, his thoughts are undifferentiated from concrete external reality so the thought, "I would like to murder my uncle" turns into, "I have murdered my uncle, and I believe I am no longer worthy of the family's love."

Over time, Mr. I.J. talked more ordinarily about his difficulties, in particular, his fears about deportation and not being able to study or enter employment and his fear he would return to a life of crime within the gang. This led the team to ensure that he was registered with a GP and placed with local services. They supported him to contact his uncle's immigration solicitor who encouraged him to begin his application for a Right to Remain, which the medical team officially endorsed. Thus, he gradually came to bear the fact that although some damage had been done to his relationship with his uncle, and also to his reputation (he had extended his criminal record), he could repair some of the damage he had done to himself in phantasy and change his assessment of himself from worthless into worthwhile.

This development in Mr. I.J. reflects a shift from the paranoid-schizoid to the depressive position as the patient becomes more able to use staff support and realistically face his difficulties. Although he seemed to experience guilt about the damage done to his relationships through his aggression and superior states of mind, there was no mention of his being deported or sent to prison. The ward team's support allowed him to establish a more realistic picture of himself and others, as well as a more realistic footing in reality (e.g. soliciting help from an immigration lawyer). Nursing staff reported that he was soon transferred to an open ward due to both improvements in his mental state and reduction in the level of risk. He was then transferred into a homeless persons' unit. Less than a month later, the PICU staff were delighted when he returned to the ward to inform them that he was being discharged and thanked them for their support.

In the case of Mr. I.J., we can see how the staff responded to different elements of the patient, just as different aspects of his personality dominated his mind. We see the oscillation with the way he deals with underlying feelings of impotence and worthlessness, either by adopting the identity of a powerful messenger of God or by becoming an intimidating and powerful gang leader controlling the ward. Although he threatened ward staff, they remained interested and engaged. The supervision group was able to support the staff in noticing things about the patient's presentation and his history. The staff were able to think about who the patient was behind the psychotic, paranoid, and/or anti-social presentation. The patient responded to this interest and engagement by warming to the staff's curiosity. The nursing staff also brought to the supervision group all sorts of information about the patient and the way he was behaving on the ward. This attitude helped them to notice and address with him his anxieties and feelings of worthlessness. Although he had done damage to his relationships through his intimidating attitude, he had not managed to either split the ward or induce a punitive response. Indeed, eventually, the caring attitude of the ward team showed him that he could be taken back into a ward "family" and offered a place, despite his difficulties.

Patients who suffer from a psychotic illness and/or personality disorder have failed to internalise a good object that can help them bear the psychic pain involved in reality testing. Consequently, their fragile egos fragment or collapse when psychic emotional conflict threatens them. They employ primitive psychotic processes to defend themselves from these threatening psychic states. In the paranoid-schizoid position, patients split the ego and project threatening aspects of the self into a bad external object. These projections are often accompanied by behaviour that elicits a response in the object that coheres with the projection. Thus Mr. I.J. in the last example defends himself from anxieties about psychotic fragmentation by adopting the identity of a powerful gangster. He projects all vulnerabilities into other patients and then attempts to control them by intimidation. In this way, he cures his fragmenting ego by adopting the identity of a powerful figure who can control others that now contain the "mad" aspects of himself. Instead of a man with psychosis living in a psychiatric hospital, he is a powerful gang leader who belongs in prison.

It is necessary to make distinctions between illness and health in order to assess the patient's capacity to make informed decisions. However, I would argue that the binary distinction between illness and health has limited explanatory value when it comes to thinking about complex clinical situations. A dynamic understanding of the patient's internal world provides a useful model for thinking about the way a patient can shift between different states of mind during different phases of their illness. The nature of Mr. I.J.'s condition required physical containment and a robust clinical team that provided medical and nursing care. The supervision group provided a place where we could gather the picture together, share impressions and perceptions, and notice the development of the patient's relationships with members of staff. Over time, the team were able to develop a dynamic formulation which changed and developed as the clinical picture changed.

Discussion

Whereas Freud (1900) described dreams as "the royal road to the unconscious," Lucas (2009a) used to describe the counter-transference as the "Royal road to the unconscious" with patients in psychotic states of mind. However, the power of the concrete projections can undermine the capacity of the person who has been projected into to separate from their immediate experience and thinking. When the staff member cannot think but "must act," they are caught up in a counter-transference response. Concrete communications tend to provoke concrete reactions, and the more violent the communication, the more difficult it is to maintain a capacity to think symbolically. Symbolic thinking requires a capacity to take in the communication and resonate with it, allowing a broad range of possible meanings to emerge. This is difficult to do when you have been physically or verbally assaulted as one's natural and appropriate reaction is to go into action. The beauty of team-working is that while one person may be literally and/or metaphorically "hit" by the effect of concrete actions and communications, other members of the team hopefully remain able to maintain their capacity to think symbolically.

This is one of the reasons that good psychiatric care tends to be related to well-led teams with good morale. Teams like this can absorb the physical, psychological, and verbal assaults that come with the work, without becoming cut-off, cynical, or inappropriately driven into action. One consultant from a PICU said he was amazed at the staff's devotion to their patients, at the quality of their work, and their resilience. This was a well-run ward with good staff and relatively low levels of staff turnover. The level of the disturbance in the patient population meant that staff were frequently assaulted, both physically and verbally, but staff refused to take prolonged periods of time off sick and continued to maintain a caring and interested attitude towards their work. This is not the same everywhere, as some units with low morale have high staff turnover, high numbers of agency staff, and high levels of staff sickness. In my experience, where these conditions exist, it can lead to rather more mechanistic and reactive approaches to care.

Acutely disturbed individuals require mental health services to take action and intervene actively in their lives, even sometimes against their will. This is an important function of psychiatry and psychiatric practice and a reluctance to act may be destructive and unhelpful. However, mental health services also need to take in and think about the meaning of their patients' symptoms, behaviours, and actions. As I have argued throughout this chapter, it is the absence of an adequate model for thinking about the effects of psychotic communication that can leave professionals in danger of reacting to unconscious forces without understanding them. Richard Lucas used to say staff need support to try and "tune in to the psychotic wavelength" (Lucas, 2009b) in order to support their patients' struggle with the psychotic aspects of the self. When staff can tune into a patient's concrete thinking, it can help avoid dangerous exchanges of words and misunderstandings. Gathering together things the patient says, as well as their enactments and concrete actions, can help the team develop a picture of what provokes verbal outbursts and/or violent actions; thereby reducing their prevalence. It is important to note that a lot of this understanding often goes on in hindsight after an incident has occurred. Nevertheless, it is valuable because it can help reduce repetitive patterns of behaviour and the resulting risk to staff from verbal or violent assault.

Hopefully, these examples show how patients' communications and actions can have disturbing effects on mental health professionals by provoking them into reacting or attempting to control the patient's thinking or behaviour. Although at times, actions taken by staff are appropriate and necessary, they may also be driven by a wish to kill off unpleasant projections from the patient because they are disturbing and destructive. However, it is incumbent upon both staff and patients to try to understand the disruptive and destructive elements in their thinking because without this deeper understanding, there will be missed opportunities, as the underlying meaning of communication is lost, ignored, or crushed.

Conclusion

Patients and staff both need defences against psychic pain. However, these defences can become unproductive when they interfere with opportunities for psychic development and growth. It is hard being with patients whose minds may be fragmented and their lives damaged by their mental illness. This can be as difficult for staff to face as it is for patients. Staff need to be helped to notice when they turn away from painful thoughts about their patients to idealised solutions like medication. Supervision groups can help support staff's curiosity and interest in their patients even when they are very ill or their behaviour is challenging.

Psychoanalytic supervision can help staff tune into the psychotic level of communication in both psychotic and personality-disordered patients. While patients need their psychotic defences from time to time, they also fear being left on their own with their psychosis. The patient needs to feel staff understand that while they are unable to face the pain and damage done to their lives through illness, they can rely on staff to support them in their fight to remain in touch with reality.

References

Bortolotti, L. (2011). Double bookkeeping in delusions: Explaining the gap between saying and doing. In J.H. Aguilar, A.A. Buckareff and K. Frankish (Eds.), *New waves in Philosophy of Action*. London: Palgrave Macmillan.

Bronstein, C. (2018). Delusion and reparation. *International Journal of Psychoanalysis, 99*(5), 1057–1074.

Freud, S. (1900). The interpretation of dreams. In *The standard edition of the complete psychological works of Sigmund Freud*, Volume 4–5 (p. 608). London: Hogarth Press.

Lucas, R. (2009a). Dreams and delusions. In D. Birksted-Breen (Ed.), *The psychotic wavelength: A psychoanalytic perspective for psychiatry* (pp. 157–165). London: Routledge.

Lucas, R. (2009b). The psychotic wavelength. In D. Birksted-Breen (Ed.), *The psychotic wavelength: A psychoanalytic perspective for psychiatry* (pp. 142–156). London: Routledge.

Rosenfeld, H. (1971). A clinical approach to the psychoanalytic theory of the life and the death instincts: An investigation of the aggressive aspects of narcissism. *International Journal of Psychoanalysis, 52*(2), 169–178.

Sohn, L. (1997). Unprovoked assaults: Making sense of apparently random violence. In D. Bell (Ed.), *Reason and passion: A celebration of the work of Hannah Segal*. Tavistock Series. London: Duckworth.

Chapter 8

Therapeutic work with treatment-resistant patients

There are certain patients who go through a repetitive cycle of discharge and readmission from psychiatric services. This group of patients will have picked up various diagnoses and been treated on numerous drug regimes. Their length of stay in clinical services is longer than average and discharge usually takes place when there is a reduction in positive symptoms of illness, along with a reduction in immediate risk, rather than any evidence of insight into their condition. This pattern often takes place many times over many years and can lead to a demoralising clinical situation. However, what are the factors underlying this dynamic? Why do some people recover while others develop a circular pattern of illness and relapse? It is certainly not purely to do with the presence of psychopathology. All of us are capable of becoming psychologically ill from time to time. Psychological health is not defined by the presence or absence of psychopathology but is rather to do with the mind's tendency to fragment or collapse under psychological pressure.

Case example 1: Manic depressive defence

The ward team presented the case of Mr. X.X., a man in his mid-30s, with a diagnosis of schizophrenia, who was repeatedly admitted to the ward in a violent psychotic state. He would be discharged and stop taking his anti-psychotic medication and be readmitted a few months later. He had a delusion that he was given power by the Sun God who had sent him to Earth to prevent Armageddon. He walked around the ward as if he was a God and used to bark orders at staff and patients alike.

Mr. X.X. also believed he was inhabited by a figure called "Reyer" who told him what to do and required looking after. For example, she liked him smoking and demanded that he smoked whenever she wanted him to. This was often the cause of arguments with staff as he did not recognise the staff's authority and need to enforce the smoking policy.

The patient refused to take anti-psychotic medication from male members of staff and when they tried, it would often lead to violent exchanges. However, he tended to have a less antagonistic relationship with older female members of staff and used to allow them to give him his medication. Mr. X.X. referred to some of the older female members of staff as "mother" and although he was often violent and intimidating on the ward, they often remarked on his underlying sensitivity.

Although Mr. X.X's mother had committed suicide many years previously, he would always insist that she was alive. This once led to an argument with his brother who came on a home visit and told staff that his brother needed to accept that his mother was dead.

My thought was that the patient's treatment-resistant state was driven by a manic fear of depression that hated any acknowledgement of his illness or need for treatment and care. He identified himself as a powerful healing figure who could keep this internal figure alive that, I suspect, represented his mother.

The consultant said that he had talked to the patient about his relationship with his mother after the incident with the brother. Although the patient denied that his mother was dead, it did seem to reach him emotionally. The ward psychologist then started to see Mr. X.X. for some trauma-focused psychological work to see if they could help reduce the reliance of manic defences as a way of defending against feelings of sadness and loss.

This work seemed to provoke a spate of violent threats and aggressive manic behaviour. However, the team realised that the patient was trying to expel threatening emotions and resisted the temptation to respond to his threats through the use of seclusion or high doses of anti-psychotic medication.

At the following meeting, the consultant mentioned that the patient had started singing in a grandiose and manic fashion while the consultant was interviewing him. The consultant waited for him to finish and then commented that the lyrics of the song were about sadness and loss. The patient's manic presentation slowed down and he seemed able to register the consultant's comments.

The team certainly felt that although the patient presented with manic and grandiose presentations, this seemed to be losing its power and the patient seemed to be more emotionally available.

Theory

Klein (1935) described the feelings of abandonment, despair, and loss experienced by the infant when faced with the damage done to the object in the early stages of the depressive position. The individual feels that they have in phantasy damaged the loved object and that they cannot repair the damage done or make amends. In their depressed state, the individual believes they have destroyed everything and have been left alone to face the desolation and despair of their internal state. This internal situation is accompanied by guilt, which in turn can lead to a collapse of the ego or a fragmentation. The individual may believe that the extent of the damage done to the object in phantasy can only be repaired using magical means. Thus, the individual goes back to the primitive psychotic defences of the paranoid-schizoid position in an attempt to cure the concrete damage.

Klein (1935) differentiates between reparation and manic reparation. Reparation is used to describe the individual's wish to symbolically repair the object as a result of damage done by aggressive attacks in phantasy. In ordinary reparation, dependence upon the object is accepted and the limitations of symbolic repair can be acknowledged. By contrast, manic reparation represents a magical wish to repair the object believed to be severely damaged. It involves concrete rather than symbolic repair and a merely superficial acknowledgement of the individual's dependence upon the object. When the individual feels that they can't repair the object, they retreat to the use of omnipotent defences in order to defend themselves against unbearable feelings of guilt.

I believe that Mr. X.X. could not bear the damage done to his ego as a consequence of his mental illness, nor could he healthily mourn his mother's suicide, and so he was persecuted by unbearable guilt. The mania meant he was constantly on the move trying to keep away from the depression and sadness that he feared might catch up with him if he slowed down. The grandiosity also meant that rather than face the fact that his illness may have had an adverse effect on his mother's health, he employed manic reparation in order to deny the reality of her death. In many ways his mania protected him from the painful realisation his mother had in fact died. Instead, he acted as if he could avoid guilt by keeping her alive inside him.

Case example 2: Projection of depression

Mr. M.N. was a man in his mid-20s who had been admitted to an acute admission ward in a manic, agitated state. The staff nurse told the supervision group he had been discharged and readmitted on numerous occasions over the last couple of years. They felt hopeless about any chance of progress or development.

Mr. M.N. had a younger sister and devoted, concerned parents who described a history of him having tantrums as a child and problems with figures of authority. His mother told staff that she had suffered from post-natal depression after both his and his younger sister's birth. She believed these episodes of post-natal depression had affected her son. She also mentioned that her sister had a diagnosis of schizophrenia.

As a child, Mr. M.N. had struggled to concentrate at school, but despite his difficulties, he had managed to get several A-levels and had gone to university. There, he apparently smoked a lot of cannabis, withdrew socially, and soon lost his place at university. He worked for a short period on a building site but gave up that work after suffering a physical injury. He joined a fanatical cult for a number of years, but they rejected him as a result of his manic breakdowns. When manic, he would become violent, set fire to his room, self-harm, take off his clothes and present himself in a sexually provocative manner, offering to perform submissive sexual acts towards female staff.

The ward staff described how on the ward he would take off his clothes and dance around the day room, behaving in a sexually disinhibited manner. The O.T.

said he was obsessed with cannabis and would spend time in the art classes drawing and painting cannabis plants. The nursing staff described a pattern of him settling down while on the ward, apparently recovering, and then being discharged to his mental health hostel, at which point, he would start taking drugs, precipitating another manic episode, and would be readmitted to the ward.

The description of him stripping off his clothes reminded me of an exhibitionistic toddler, while his drug-taking seemed driven by a need to get away from any awareness of himself and his situation. The sexualisation also seemed designed to excite others as well as himself. In response to my comments, nursing staff described the way he would interfere if his primary nurse was talking to another patient, but would sometimes settle down if she spoke to him calmly and reassuringly. But then, at a certain point, he would become distracted or try to insert some sexual suggestion into the conversation.

I thought the mother's reports of her post-natal depression were relevant and important. Mr. M.N. reminded me of the infants of post-natally depressed mothers on the mother and baby unit, who either become depressed in response to their mother's lack of responsiveness or become distracted and agitated. It was as if he missed a mother who could help him gather himself together but was like an infant who was dealing with a depressed mother whom he could not interest or excite. Not only did the sexualised behaviour seem to be a way of exciting himself, but I was also struck by his wish to excite others through his dancing and sexually provocative behaviour. The use of drugs and his mania seemed to be an active attempt to keep his mind and his anxieties at a distance, as if he was terrified of thinking about himself. The toddler-like exhibitionism enabled him to behave in a manner that evaded any responsibility for his actions. One could argue that Mr. M.N. used his mania to evacuate underlying feelings of depression about his situation into his parents or the ward staff. He then felt threatened by their anxieties about his condition and attempted to cure them of their worry by injecting them with his sexualised excitement and exhibitionistic behaviour. As if the answer to all anxieties and concerns was excitement. I was struck by the story of him having to give up work after sustaining a physical injury at work as if any damage sustained led to a total collapse in his view of himself. In a way, he was like a man that continually tried to maintain a state of mindlessness, forcing his parents and the ward team to do the worrying for him.

In the supervision group, we talked about the need to talk to him about his tendency to become manic and excited as a way of getting away from his worries and anxieties about himself. I thought it was also important to think about discharge plans as he seemed to be clearly indicating that he did not feel able to manage his own life independently and would struggle to resist the temptation to develop a manic state of mind which offered relief from the depressing realities of his situation.

Although the parents offered to have him move back in with them, he refused, saying that he needed his space. The lack of a discharge plan that took account of his manic mental state had led to a fruitless pattern of discharge and readmission.

Thus, he punished his parents for failing to provide him with ideal care in the first place by acting out his inability to think realistically about himself and his needs. He projected responsibility for, and anxiety about, his level of functioning into his parents, who then had to go on worrying about their son while he showed no signs of any need to change.

Bion (1957) outlined the way the mother takes in the infant's feelings of being overwhelmed and thinks about the experience for the baby. The mother then responds in a way that communicates that she has not only taken the appropriate action to deal with the problem but also understood how the baby feels. This model of thought and loving attitude is then internalised to form the basis of the infant's capacity to think about themselves as a sentient human being. Bion (1958) describes the failure of the mother to contain the infant's projections as a psychic catastrophe that leads to the development of an "ego destructive super ego" rather than allowing the internalisation of a good internal object. This "ego destructive super ego" is against dependent object relationships that involve the acknowledgement of the need for the object. So instead of an ego that supports the development of vulnerable aspects of the personality, their minds are dominated by a "super ego that criticises and mocks" any sign of weakness. Patients whose minds are dominated by this sort of ego develop relationships based on the principles of triumph, contempt, and control in order to master feelings of dependency that threaten the ego's view of itself. Mr. M.N. showed no signs of having developed a mind capable of thinking about himself and his situation. He seemed committed to a mindless state, represented by the idealisation of cannabis and a child-like state represented by the tendency to take his clothes off in public. Rivière (1936) highlighted the difficulty some patients have facing guilt, as they fear integration and the depressive position will lead to the emergence of a catastrophic situation. They have an omnipotent sense of responsibility for damage done to themselves and their object and believe awareness of this situation will lead to either suicide or mental fragmentation.

The patient's unconscious grievances towards his mother for her post-natal depression and then having his younger sister was evident in his thoughtless attitude towards his life and his care. He can't move on from being an infant in need of care who is being asked to wait before he can be sorted and so stays in that infantile state. In a way, he maintains a view that he is unable to take responsibility for himself and has no choice but to act mindlessly. All concern about his repetitive pattern of behaviour is located in the staff and his parents. This pushes his parents and the authorities into a position where they take either some or all responsibility for him or the pattern of discharge and readmission will continue. In his mindless state, he needed a supporting structure around him that could take some responsibility for his care, while sharing anxieties and concerns about his life with him.

There is a danger that this sort of situation can produce a moralistic response, as authorities force the individual to take responsibility for their irresponsible behaviour. The problem with this is that it treats the individual as if he was capable of managing his emotional life and his mind, and this fails to recognise the level of the individual's disturbance. Like a child with a precociously developed intellect that outstrips their emotional maturity.

Case example 3: Idealisation as a defence

The ward occupational therapist (OT) presented the case of Mr. O.P., a man in his early 20s with delusional beliefs about his ex-girlfriend. This is an example of a revolving door situation where mania is followed by discharge resulting in ensuing cycles of relapse and readmission. Mr. O.P. was described as a highly gifted university student who was heading for a first-class degree until he broke down, after seeing a picture of his girlfriend with another man on holiday. This provoked a depressive collapse in that he stopped eating, withdrew to his bedroom, and dropped out of university. Several months before the admission to hospital, he started to become manic. On one occasion, he attacked his father who had objected to the patient's sexually inappropriate gestures and comments towards his sister and mother. The admitting team recorded that the parents did not believe in medication and described their son's behaviour as a stress reaction. The parents spent several months trying to manage their son's disturbed state at home. His younger brother eventually persuaded the parents to contact psychiatric services as the parents had started to argue over the management of Mr. O.P. On assessment, he expressed delusional beliefs about his ex-girlfriend and commented that he had been sent to save her from the Devil's influence. The parents gave a glowing history of their son's achievements. In addition to being a gifted academic, he was described as a gifted sportsman.

In discussion with the group, the staff emphasised the parent's insistence on their son's abilities and concern that he should get back to his studies as quickly as possible. They also mentioned his obsession with his body and his looks as he spent hours in the gym working on his physical appearance and looking at himself in the mirror. It was as if he had to be maintained by himself and his parents as a "God-like" figure with no faults (like Narcissus gazing at his perfect image in the mirror). Mr. O.P.'s mesmeric admiration for his perfect looks ignores the evidence of damage and fragmentation in his mind. The parents' description of their son's illness as stress-related and the emphasis on getting him back to his studies minimised the seriousness of his condition. The younger brother, who had originally encouraged the parents to seek help, seemed more able to see the extent of his brother's problem.

Mr. O.P. identified with his parent's view of him as a "God-like" figure who was perfect in every way. I am of the view that when he saw his ex-girlfriend with another man, his view of himself as his parent's perfect son was punctured. After the collapse, he develops a delusional belief that he is sent by God to rescue his girlfriend from the Devil. The belief is that the ideal state that existed before the breakdown would be restored if only he could persuade his girlfriend to come back to him. Thus, he can magically undo the damage the betrayal is believed to have caused. His girlfriend's betrayal is also seen to be part of some magical demonic process rather than driven by her own free will. I suspect this was a repetition of a depressive collapse in his mind as an infant, provoked by the birth of his younger brother. He must have felt his mother's betrayal by having another child meant he was unloved and unlovable. The timing of the breakdown was also connected to the upcoming exams at the university where anything other than a first would be experienced by him as a failure. The patient seems to carry the weight of his parents' expectations of perfection as well as his own. Loss of the ideal situation seems to threaten the patient and the family with anxieties about a catastrophic collapse. There is no room in this system for ordinary human limitations or weakness, including psychological fragility in the face of rejection or loss. The capacity to face reality seemed to be located in the younger brother, who the staff feel is most in touch with his brothers' condition. Steiner (2018) describes the way the picture of the ideal family is often used to defend against trauma. Sometimes this trauma is related to a difficulty facing ordinary losses associated with competition and rejection. It is as if the family has to maintain a picture of themselves as being ideal with no ordinary human failings.

In the group, we discussed the need to help the patient come to terms with his situation by talking about his difficulty acknowledging his anxieties. We also talked about the need to engage the parents in a realistic discussion about their son and his condition. Staff were worried about upsetting the parents and making them worry. I thought this response was counter-transference as staff felt unconsciously obliged to support the parents in their idealised picture of their son. The parents, like the patient, continually attempted to eradicate any blemish—like the son's preoccupation with his perfect looks. The rigidly defended, idealised position meant there was no room to mourn the loss of the ideal. Klein (1935) outlined the way idealisation is often driven by a fear of fragmentation, as if the loss of the ideal heralds an unmanageable psychic collapse. In my experience, a change of perspective in these intransigent psychic states needs to take place in the therapist, or in this case the psychiatric team, before it can take place in the patient. The psychiatric team caring for the patient needed to separate from the effect of the counter-transference and find a compassionate way of talking to the patient and his family about his difficulties and thus provide a more realistic picture of his potential for recovery.

Case example 4: Repetitive acting out

A consultant psychiatrist presented Mr. Q.R., a man in his mid-20s with a long-standing relationship with mental health settings. He was transferred to the psychiatric intensive care unit (PICU) and nursed on one-to-one nursing observations as a result of his self-harming and dangerous fire setting, both prior to admission and again when on the open ward. He had also had one spell in seclusion, following his threatening behaviour towards a staff member, who had asked him to adhere to a ward rule. In the early stages of his admission, he continually asked to be transferred to prison and out of the psychiatric system.

Mr. Q.R.'s mother had suffered a breakdown after his father had left her with Mr. Q.R., when he and his sister who had Down's syndrome were both very young. After several years, the school contacted social services because they were concerned that the children appeared to be neglected and were showing behavioural problems at school. As a consequence of an investigation, social services decided the mother was unable to cope and removed the children, placing them under the care of the father and his new family. His mother then died when Mr. Q.R. was in his early teens and his behaviour deteriorated further. Several years later, the patient's father contacted social services saying that they could not cope with Mr. Q.R.'s disruptive and dangerous behaviour. The father believed his son had set fire to the house, causing considerable damage.

The primary nurse mentioned that some of the most serious incidents of fire setting and self-harm had occurred preceding a court hearing or when he was informed that his level of observations would be reduced, or his Mental Health Act section discontinued. Indeed, any reduction in his level of care provoked violent acting out which then would force staff to reinstate high levels of observation and care. I was impressed by the way staff responded to his immaturity and vulnerability in a caring, thoughtful way despite his provocative, threatening, and demanding behaviour. However, the staff team also expressed their frustration at feeling rather trapped by this repetitive clinical situation. They described him following particular members of staff around the ward in a possessive child-like way, resenting any interference from others. Indeed, the patient sometimes gave advice to his primary nurse as if he believed that he was there to support him and not the other way around. He said that sometimes the patient tried to cheer him up when he came on shift, as if he had to make the nurse feel better.

I thought Mr. Q.R. lacked a psychological structure capable of metabolising and reflecting upon emotions. Instead, he felt compelled to evacuate his raw emotional state through actions. The lack of any internal part of his mind capable of self-reflection meant he had very little understanding of why he did what he did. The patient gave the impression of being a deprived child who had been left with a mother who was in a collapsed state and unable to cope with the demands of her situation. He gave the impression of being angry and prone to outbursts of anger through his acting out whenever he felt rejected. However, I think the patient developed a phantasy that he was responsible for looking after his mother. This was re-enacted on the ward in relation to his primary nurse as despite his level of dependency and need he believed that he was responsible for looking after him and not the other way around. Thus, all need for care was projected into his nurse, whom he then tried to look after once he became the nurse's carer in his mind.

This illusory situation denied the reality of his relative inability to care for his mother or indeed her inability to care adequately for him. The illusion of him being able to care for his mother in this "folie à deux" broke down when he and his sister were removed by social services and sent to his father. Again, I was reminded of the primary nurse's comments about the patient's possessiveness and resentment towards their relationship with any other patients on the ward.

Any separation from the object threatened the patient's view of himself as being central to the object's preoccupation.

The fire setting at his father's house seemed to be related to his grievance towards his father and his new family for leaving him and his sister with his mother. It also seemed to represent his fury at being taken away from his mother, thus leading to a collapse in his phantasy of being the mother's ideal partner. Any threat to this close, illusory relationship produced violent self-harming or violent behaviour or fire setting. This acting out was driven by a wish to evacuate psychic states that threatened to overwhelm the patient.

Mr. Q.R. shows no evidence of having an internal object that can help him manage the demands of reality. Instead, he seeks to establish and maintain a mythically ideal relationship with an external object. He projects the feelings of vulnerability and need into the external object, whom he then cares for and controls. The patient believes he is looking after the external object in his phantasy. Any separation between himself and his object threatens to overwhelm the patient as the projected elements of his mind return. Thus vulnerable aspects of himself return and boomerang back into the ego, threatening to overwhelm the individual's psychic equilibrium. Any sign of progress became a threat, as he worried that intensive nursing care would be stopped. The patient's provocative acting out forces the staff to continue high levels of observation and care necessary to maintain his psychic equilibrium. In this way, the patient's control of the clinical environment is an attempt to avoid a repeat of the traumatic feelings associated with separation and loss of omnipotence. The situation outlined above prevents any movement or development in the clinical situation.

Again, I think the shift in approach needs to happen in the clinical team before it can happen in the patient. I suggested that the team needed to address the issue of the patient's fear that he would break down without his one-to-one support. They might try to discuss with him that he was afraid that he could not cope without high levels of nursing observations but that the team were confident they could find a way to help him manage without one-to-one care. They understood that this might make him angry from time to time but that the staff team would be able to talk to him about that and help him manage his emotions. In keeping with this approach, they might take the view that this is a man whose emotional development is arrested at a very early age and that he needs the same kind of support and encouragement to find his capacities as a young child would. The staff team very much identified with the fact that they were dealing with someone who despite his chronological age, was very immature in his emotional development.

Several weeks later, the staff team reported that there had been a reduction in the level of one-to-one observations without any incidents of self-harm. They also reported on the fact that he had responded well to the positive support and encouragement to do things and manage things on his own. Although I was sure there would be a return to his acting out behaviour if staff lost touch with the underlying level of anxiety, I thought we had discovered a way of moving things forward even if it was a question of two steps forward and one step back.

Discussion

The patients described in this chapter were lacking an internal object that could help them manage the psychic pain involved in the depressive position. When faced with feelings of guilt about the damage done to their objects, they become overwhelmed by persecutory guilt. The ego, which brings awareness of the psychic situation, is attacked and projected into the external world. Lucas (2009a) outlines the way the manic state of mind represents a rebellion against this crushing internal situation. He described it as being like a coiled spring that suddenly bursts into life throwing off the influence of the crushing super ego. Long-standing grievances against failed ideal objects also drive the rebellion. This can lead to a burst of triumphant activity and mania: "Look I do not need anyone. I can do this all myself." This activity is often driven by a narcissistic part of the individual that wishes to prove that they are independent and don't need anyone. Thus, rather than mourn the loss of the ideal self, the individual seeks magical solutions to problems and develops a mind that avoids, rather than faces, psychic realities. In this way the patient triumphs over painful feelings of guilt about the damage done to the object they depend upon. The vacuum in the ego caused by projection is then filled either with a delusional system or with a rigidly held, over-valued idea, both of which offer the ego an illusory coherence and structure. The delusional system also protects the individual from the demanding and threatening task of reality testing. Delusional systems often contain identifications with powerful figures capable of repairing underlying feelings of collapse, fragmentation, and damage.

Care and attention need to be paid to the role played by manic states of mind in the pattern of discharge and relapse. Psychiatric staff need to recognise the influence of manic states of mind and empathise with the patients' fear of reality. Although some patients say they prefer their psychosis and their mania, these states of mind can do substantial damage to the structure of their lives as meaningful relationships with work, finances, and/or personal relationships may be undermined. Patients who get lost in manic states also demonstrate moments of depressive thinking when they become concerned about the damaging effect of the mania. For example, Mr. Q.R. was recorded as saying that he needs more medication because he worries his mania will interfere with his studies. At times this is represented by something patients say; at other times the sane awareness of the illness is projected into others. The side of the patient that is concerned about the loss of contact with reality needs recognition and help in standing up to the influence of the psychotic part of the patient's mind.

Rey (1988) highlighted the way patients brought their damaged and dying internal objects alive and brought them to the analyst to be treated. The problem is that these objects are often treated by the patient as if they were concrete objects that exist within the internal world, and when these concrete objects are damaged, they believe they need concrete solutions. Rey also described the way the patient seeks manic phallic solutions to a feeling that they contain a destroyed maternal figure. Symbolic reparation is not felt to be sufficient to cure the object; therefore, the individual feels compelled to seek magical solutions, otherwise known as manic reparation. When this breaks down, the individual turns to attempts to minimise and control psychic vulnerability and pain. Staff on in-patient units will often say that they prefer it when patients are in a manic mood as they are easier to be with. It is common for patients in a manic state of mind to noisily dominate the attention in the in-patient units. This atmosphere is designed to drown out the underlying depressive affect and communications that are also invariably present.

Minne (2008) makes the point that patients need support in developing knowledge of who they are and what they are like. However, she also points out that this knowledge can traumatise the patient as he/she becomes aware of the extent of their difficulties. Hence patients need support in getting to know themselves. Sometimes they need an exoskeleton around them that can represent reality and the care they need for some time. Staff need to be supported in standing up to the pressure to collude with their patient's psychotic belief either that they do not need support and care or that they can be discharged from psychiatric services without it being provided in their follow-up. This is often argued about in terms of respecting the patient's wishes. Of course, mental health professionals should always listen to their patients' wishes but with a clinical ear using their hard-won clinical judgement.

Freud (1920) outlined the way we are likely to repeat traumatic situations that we fail to understand, and indeed, patients often repeat patterns of behaviour without it becoming evident what the pattern represents. There are a group of patients who have been institutionalised from a young age due to deprivation, parental mental illness, or personality disorder. The patients are often very dependent upon institutional care as they lack an ego that can think about themselves in a mature way.

Lucas (2009b) described psychotic patients needing an exoskeleton around them that could represent reality and help the patient resist the pull towards their delusional worlds. This is particularly important when dealing with patients who have very little capacity to bear the emotional pain and are continually lulled by the attraction of manic states.

I am often struck by the fact that manic elements that deny the extent of the difficulties often drown out depressive communications that communicate concern about the damage being done in the patient's relationship with reality. Patients need staff to listen out for depressed states that are either projected acted out or drowned out by mania. This part of the personality may be the most amenable to therapeutic work. However, it is also difficult to identify and may be undermined by contempt or drowned out by the noise coming from manic, aggressive, and/or psychotic parts of the personality. Recovery is dependent upon the patient's ability to find support for healthy aspects of the personality. It is not possible to eradicate disturbed or destructive aspects of the personality even though our patients sometimes wish we could surgically remove their illness. However, staff can help support healthy aspects of the personality and help the patient differentiate between states of mind based on the avoidance of reality and states of mind that help the patient face reality.

Staff in psychiatric settings often have to work with treatment-resistant patients over long periods of time, and during that time the mania and activity may dominate the clinical picture. I think it is helpful if one can use supervision to try and identify the things that send patients into regressive acting out or into psychotic states and look out for depressive elements of the patient's presentation. Once depressive states of mind have been identified, it may be possible to talk to the patient about their worries and concerns. This can strengthen the patient's capacity to bear painful realities and reduce the dependence on violent splitting and projection. It is important for staff to bear in mind that words may also be used as a form of evacuation as the fact that someone says things does not necessarily mean that they are applying that insight to themselves. It might be an example of evacuation through use of words. Patients with long-standing severe and enduring mental illness and personality disorder need long-term support and different settings as they move between different states of mind. They are liable to relapse without adequate support as they may not have sufficient positive "facts" available to keep them "well."

Conclusion

There are certain patients that lack an internal structure that can help them bear the pain of integration as they are threatened by feelings of fragmentation or suicidal states due to persecutory anxiety. These patients seek refuge by evacuating their minds and then living in delusional systems of their creation that avoid painful reality testing. Once discharged from psychiatric settings these patients are left at the mercy of these manic and psychotic aspects of themselves. In this state, they quickly deteriorate, as the extent of their illness interferes with any ordinary ego functioning. In addition, they often feel they carry around a reproachful damaged object that threatens them with unconscious guilt and depression. In desperation, they employ manic mechanisms that deny psychic reality and use omnipotent defences against psychic pain. Depressing realities are continually evacuated as they threaten to persecute the patient. There may be a driven attempt to avoid this unconscious guilt that is felt to threaten the patient's mind with either fragmentation or collapse. Thinking about the factors that trigger these collapses might not eradicate the problem, but it can help staff with their feelings of frustration about cases that defeat them. This can then help with morale and help staff maintain a sympathetic approach to their patients.

References

Bion, W. R. (1957). Differentiation of the psychotic from the non-psychotic personalities. *International Journal of Psychoanalysis, 38*(3–4), 266–275. In *Second thoughts: Selected papers on psychoanalysis.* New York, NY: Jason Aronson.

Bion, W. R. (1958). On arrogance. *International Journal of Psychoanalysis*, *39*, 341–346.

Freud (1920). Beyond the pleasure principle. In *The standard edition of the complete psychological works of Sigmund Freud*, Volume 18, (pp. 3–64). London: Hogarth Press.

Klein, M. (1935). A contribution to the psychogenesis of manic-depressive states. *International Journal of Psychoanalysis*, *16*, 145–174.

Lucas, R. (2009a). Why the cycle in a clinical psychosis? A psychoanalytic perspective on recurrent manic depressive psychosis. In D. Birksted-Breen (Ed.), *The psychotic wavelength: A psychoanalytic perspective for psychiatry*. London: Routledge.

Lucas, R. (2009b). Developing an exoskeleton. In D. Birksted-Breen (Ed.), *The psychotic wavelength: A psychoanalytic perspective for psychiatry*. London: Routledge.

Minne, C. (2008). The dreaded and dreading patient and therapist. In J. Gordon, G. Kirtchuk & K. London (Eds.), *Psychic assaults and frightened clinicians*. London: Karnac Books.

Rey, H. (1988). That which patients bring to analysis. *International Journal of Psychoanalysis*, *69*(4), 457–470.

Riviere, J. (1936). A contribution to the analysis of negative therapeutic reaction. *International Journal of Psychoanalysis*, *17*, 304–320.

Steiner, J. (2018). The trauma and disillusionment of Oedipus. *International Journal of Psychoanalysis*, *99*(33), 555–568.

Chapter 9

The contribution of psychoanalytic perspectives on the patient's relationship with their bodies

In this chapter I will describe four patients with different relationships with their bodies. The first example describes a man who had pain in his gut. The second patient had a tormented relationship with her Crohn's disease. The third patient had formed an identity around her disability, and the fourth had internalised a sado-masochist relationship with her body. As well as demonstrating the way psychotherapeutic treatment can promote change in the relationship between their minds and their bodies, all four demonstrate the way psychic pain can be expressed through the body.

Freud (1923) states that the ego is "first and foremost a bodily ego." In this chapter, I will look at the way the body can be used as a vessel for containing psychic pain. Indeed, patients' attitude towards themselves and their relationship with internal figures is often communicated in a concrete way through their bodies. Sifneos (1975) wrote on people suffering from "alexithymia," while Marty and D'Uzan's (1963) work on patients with a "pensée operatoire" addresses similar ways in which people present with marked absences of emotional expressiveness. These are defensive states of mind in which emotional conflicts appear to be displaced into the body, giving rise to physical symptoms.

Case example 1: "I feel it in my stomach"

Mr. S.T. was a 45-year-old man who was referred to psychotherapy after an initial discussion between the psychotherapist and the patient's consultant gastroenterologist. The patient suffered from persistent and chronic irritable bowel syndrome (IBS). He was a successful professional man in a highly pressurised job.

At the start of the consultation, Mr. S.T. looked irritated and sounded dismissive about his referral. When I asked him why he had been referred, he said that he did not know, as the consultant gastroenterologist had not discussed the referral with him. When I asked him why he had come, he said because his mood was affected by the debilitating effects of his symptoms, including stomach gripes when he eats, violent diarrhoea, and wind. He went on to explain that he was leading a re-organisation at his workplace that involved cutting staff. I asked him to tell me a bit more about the work situation. Mr. S.T. explained that budget cuts meant that he had to make people redundant. He said this was upsetting and the existing staff were already under intense pressure due to previous cuts in the service. He looked in pain as he talked about the requirement to release staff, some of whom he had known a long time and for whom he had a great deal of respect. I talked to him about the fact that he thought he was in an impossible situation—cutting valuable staff while piling more pressure on existing staff—who were already under pressure. He became angry when talking about the higher management system that appeared to deny the significance of these cuts.

Mr. S.T.: They deny it all and they talk as if they have perfectly reasonable expectations when in effect the cuts have decimated my department over the last five years.

Therapist: You believe you should be able to protect the service and get angry when you cannot do anything to protect something that is so valuable. You talk as if you believe that management could do something about it if they wanted too.

Mr. S.T.: No, it's the hypocrisy I can't stand. They turn a blind eye to what's going on, they lie to themselves.

Therapist: Have you ever thought that this anger and conflict may go into your body and affect your guts?

Mr. S.T.: No, my IBS is a physical problem and when I am able to look after my diet and pay attention to what I eat, it gets better. I don't know why my gastroenterologist referred me to you. I don't have mental problems.

Therapist: However, you do feel you are being palmed off by the gastroenterologist and this enrages you. That sounds very similar to your experiences with management at work.

Mr. ST.: Yes, really he is saying there is nothing wrong with me and that I am exaggerating the problem.

Therapist: Making a fuss over nothing.

He went on to explain that his parents didn't talk about emotions during his childhood and that he was only looked after by his mother when he had a physical problem. Mr. S.T. said that his mother was a rather cold woman and his father emotionally in tune but ineffective at home.

Background

Mr. S.T. felt angry with the gastroenterologist for referring him to psychotherapy. He believed that the gastroenterologist was ducking his responsibilities by suggesting that there may be a psychological component to his physical symptoms. Like the complaint against the management at work, he felt he was being left with responsibility for managing a painful situation on his own and without help. Psychological assistance did not count as help but more like an attempt at trying to ameliorate him by smoothing things over. However, he felt that the gastroenterologist could find the solution to his symptoms if only he could be both-ered and shamed into action. Towards the end of the consultation, he explained that his mother did not "do" emotions and although he was well cared for physi-cally, he did not get much "love." He said this contemptuously as if the word had to be spat out rather than said. However, he did sound bitter when he talked about being sent off to boarding school by his father in order to "toughen him up." When I asked why his father felt he needed to be toughened up, he said that he had dif-ficulty separating from his mother, staying away from school to be with her. He said he often had headaches or stomach aches as a child.

After meeting Mr. S.T. for the first consultation, I talked to the referring gas-troenterologist. He said that the patient seemed to be content with investigations, dietary advice, and medication even though the painful symptoms persisted. However, the patient became most unhappy and complained at the suggestion of a psychological component to his IBS and the referral to the psychotherapist. The gastroenterologist said that the patient had asked if he was suggesting the problem was all in his mind. The gastroenterologist explained to the patient that he believed his bowel still needed ongoing medical care, but he also thought his stressful work and the accompanying emotional state was contributing to his physical state.

Discussion

In many ways, I thought the conflict in Mr. S.T.'s guts represented his internal conflict as he cannot bear to face the psychic pain underpinning his present situ-ation. He had a view of himself as a heroic figure who could protect important people around him. However, he could not protect his department from the cur-rent round of cuts (a national problem) and this threatened his view of himself as a "heroic rescuer." The internal conflict also then gets externalised, as rather than facing the depressing reality of his limitations, he locates the wish for a heroic rescuer into the management who, like his mother, are emotionally unavailable. He then retreats into a grievance towards them for failing to be the powerful ideal figures he wants them to be. His body—which contains these violent feelings—is then presented to the gastroenterologist who is expected to provide care and treatment.

Bion (1962) described the way undigested psychic contents, which he called "beta elements," threaten to overwhelm the infant's primitive ego. Beta elements are like raw psychic data that can't be digested or thought about and the infant evacuates them through a process of evacuation otherwise known as a projection, in order to restore the ego's psychic equilibrium. Bion argued that beta elements are projected into the external world in phantasy via physical gestures which might include any or all of the following: screaming, aggressive staring, spitting, vomiting, physical movements, or through excrement or urine. When these beta elements can be received by the mother, who responds to the infant's distress, the mother's reception of the beta element transforms it into an "alpha element." Alpha elements are psychic contents that can be thought about. The maternal capacity to think about the infant's experience and then communicate it back to the infant in a way that conveys a loving attitude is what Bion termed "reverie." Over time, the infant internalises the mother's capacity to think about psychic experiences. This is the basis of the infant's good internal object and forms the foundation of the ego's capacity to think about emotional experiences.

When there is a breakdown in the mother-infant relationship, it can reduce the infant's capacity to metabolise psychic states. Instead of evacuating the beta elements into a mother who can contain them, the infant continues to rely on primitive psychic defences like splitting and projection. In this state of mind, the infant's fragile ego feels threatened by the presence of concrete physical pain. Segal (1957) described these states of mind as symbolic equations. These symbolic equations lack the representative quality necessary for symbolic thought and must be evacuated as they pose a threat to the infant's ego. Projections are directed either towards the external world or into the body. Indeed, Bell (2001) noted the tendency of some patients to locate bad figures in the body which they then attack by self-harming. One patient I saw in once-weekly psychotherapy carved the message "Fat Pig" on her breasts. This patient hated her femininity and any association with her mother. She thought that breasts were soft, vulnerable, and "disgusting"—something she could not stand in herself—as it reminded her of her dependence upon her mother whom she believed had failed to care for her adequately.

Alternatively, the breakdown of the relationship between mother and infant can lead to an insecure attachment and difficulty in separating (Britton, 1989). The infant tries to possess the mother as a feeling object that is always there for them and sensitive to their feelings. The relationship is threatened by any separation which introduces a threatening feeling of absence, which in turn provokes thoughts about the less-than-ideal nature of the relationship. This sort of thoughtful examination is often resisted as it is felt to threaten the patient's need for care and is often associated with blame. It is as if the opportunity to think about what is going on *in* the body, or about the patient's relationship *with* their body as a symbol of their relationship with themselves, is threatening and experienced as a persecution.

In the consultation, Mr. S.T. talked about his mother's coldness and difficulty in dealing with emotions. I think he was identified with a mother who could only relate to his physical self, not his emotional self, which seemed split-off and excluded. The relationship with his mother is replicated in his relationship with his feelings, as the body is believed to be worthy of care, while his mind and his emotions are not. It was as if he hadn't been helped to integrate mind and body fully. However, rage towards the emotionally unavailable mother is reignited in his rage towards the emotionally cut-off management team, who do not seem to be interested in the impossibility of his situation. Without a mother to care for his emotional needs, he pushes unmanageable psychological states ("beta elements"[1])

---

1 For a full account of beta elements, see Chapter 2.

into his body. He then presents the physical problems to the gastroenterologist as if he is going to his mother, saying, "Look at the pain in my body," just as he did with his stomach and headaches as a child. Mr. S.T. appears to be happy with the consultant's care of his symptoms until he mentions a referral to the psychotherapist, whereupon the patient feels betrayed and let down. At this moment, it is as if the gastroenterologist is threatening to take the physical care of the body away while locating all the problems in the mind. This is the case even though the gastroenterologist reassured the patient that he needed ongoing physical care from him.

Mr. S.T. is so traumatised by the idea of the referral that he only hears that he is being discharged from physical care. The referral is also experienced as a threat because it brings psychic states that have been projected into the body back into the mind. This threatens his psychic equilibrium. In many ways, one might think of projections into the body as an attempt to protect the mind from threatening feelings. I believe the referral is experienced as a traumatic repetition of his early experience, in which his father deals with his insecure attachment to the mother (that cares for his body) by sending him off to boarding school, leading to a brutal separation. Thus, the body is experienced as something that contains persecutory emotional experiences that the patient would like to have physically removed.

The psychotherapist is felt to be like the father who advises the gastroenterologist to send him off for psychotherapy as a solution to his physical problems. The patient feels that he is being denied real care in order to "toughen him up." In the following session, I was able to explore his fears of being abandoned by the medical team and reassured him that they would remain involved and that we saw his clinical condition as needing joint care. This session seemed to help Mr. S.T. settle into psychotherapy.

Case example 2: The emotional impact of patients with chronic physical conditions

A clinical nurse specialist in an inflammatory bowel disorder (IBD) service presented the case of Mrs. U.V., a 35-year-old woman, who had suffered from Crohn's disease since her late teens. She had had many operations on her gut and these operations had themselves caused complications. Several years ago, she was admitted to the intensive therapy unit in a life-threatening condition as a result of an outbreak.

The Crohn's disease had interfered with every aspect of Mrs. U.V.'s life in an intrusive and disabling way. For example, she was unemployed, as the symptoms and her preoccupations with them interfered with her everyday functioning. The patient was married to a supportive husband and they wanted to start a family. Several years ago, she had conceived, but the baby was severely damaged and died in utero. It was not clear whether the Crohn's had any influence on the outcome of the pregnancy. Mrs. U.V. wanted to undertake IVF which she believed would improve her life and her situation. However, the process required her to stop taking her Crohn's medication for a few months and there never seemed to be a period when she felt free of physical symptoms.

Nurse-patient relationship

The patient continually asked for reassurance about the right time to stop the Crohn's medication in order to commence the medical procedure. This is an example of a conversation with Mrs. U.V.

Mrs. U.V: Is this a good time to stop the medication?
IBD nurse specialist: Well, how are you feeling?
Mrs. U.V.: I'm Ok.
IBD nurse specialist: Well obviously you are concerned. But although we can't guarantee you won't relapse, the Crohn's is fairly well controlled at the moment.
Mrs. U.V.: I have a slight cold at the moment.

This communication leaves the nurse feeling that she should encourage the patient to take a risk but then worrying she would have encouraged her to do something reckless if either the patient has a relapse or the pregnancy is unsuccessful. This circular conversation occurs every few weeks.

In this brief interaction, the nurse is left feeling guilty because the Crohn's is depriving the patient of the life she wishes to have.

In addition to meeting with patients under their care, the department at the hospital had a helpline and email access to a team of nurse specialists. Mrs. U.V. will call and speak to a member of staff or leave a message or send an email at any time during the day or night. The calls and communications are numerous and usually come across as a request for reassurance regarding a physical symptom. These symptoms are not necessarily connected to the Crohn's. For example, she reports back on all medical consultations with her GP, for example, coughs or colds. The patient also asks questions about the impact of the disorder on her life.

Mrs. U.V.: My husband has asked me to go on holiday abroad, but I'm not sure if I should go?
Nurse: Why wouldn't you go?
Mrs. UV: What happens if I have an outbreak of Crohn's?

This interchange puts pressure on the nurse to know what Mrs. U.V. should do. As if she could predict the likelihood of relapse. The patient has had Crohn's for many years and knows that Crohn's is unpredictable by nature. The question leaves the nurse feeling responsible for the patient's life in an unrealistic way, as she feels under pressure to give her advice. She is either depriving the patient of having a life if she advises against the risk or taking responsibility for the consequences for the patient if she says, "Go on holiday."

The nurse described how she dreaded the calls and emails because she often felt the life was being sucked out of her. This made her feel guilty as she knows Mrs. U.V. has a disabling physical condition that causes considerable suffering and seriously interferes with her life and her possibility of having children.

The nurse explained that this experience contrasts with her feelings about another patient who has a similar physical condition. Ms. X.Y. had also nearly died as a result of her illness and from time to time she had to be admitted to hospital. The nurse explained that this patient would phone the team after an episode, explaining what had happened, then, as a result of her knowledge of her condition she would make appropriate suggestions about the next step. It was evident the patient had an active life, making the most of her talents as an artist. On one occasion recently, the patient contacted the team saying that she was feeling a bit vulnerable as a result of a relapse of her illness. The patient saw members of the team and the psychological anxiety resolved itself and she was restored to her former state, which might be described as Ms. X.Y. having the appropriate level of self-management without being recklessly independent. The patient often took efforts to spare the staff team's time, apologising for the demands her illness made upon them. The nurse reported her different feelings with the two patients. With Ms. X.Y., the contact was always felt to be necessary, useful, and appropriate to her current state of mind. This was different to the experience with Mrs. U.V. where the nurse specialist felt guilty, stuck, and frustrated as the communication often felt like it was going around in circles. The nurse said she sometimes felt like the patient was acting like a "wingeing child" who made endless demands, whereas Ms. X.Y. tried to use the support offered to re-establish her independent existence and health.

Discussion

So, how do we understand the difference in the counter-transference of this nurse to these two patients?

What is apparent is that Ms. X.Y. has accepted her condition and adapted to its demands. Although the illness disrupts her capacity to have a "normal" life, it is apparent that she has accepted the illness as a part of her. She takes responsibility for the illness and the treatment of the illness in order to minimise its influence so that she can get on with her life. This involves trying to adopt a mature response to the anxiety caused by her condition when she can. She regresses to the point of feeling like a vulnerable child when she is overwhelmed by anxiety if her condition becomes more serious, but then recovers her capacity to manage herself when her physical condition improves.

I think we could say that Ms. X.Y. has mourned the loss of the life she may have had without Crohn's. She may not like it, but she has learned to accommodate the disability the illness imposes, so that she can make the best of her life. She wants to live as full a life as possible while accepting that her health is unreliable and fragile. There may be areas in her life that have stolen opportunities from her. For example, she does not mention having a family or relationships. We have no idea why this is, but one could imagine that she might have painful feelings of loss associated with these areas. However, one gets the impression that she is keen to make as much of life as she can and tries to find ways of adapting to the limitations the illness puts upon her without being defined by it. This does not involve denying the illness, as this will increase the likelihood of relapse and further illness. However, it does mean that she does not allow the illness to take over her life. The nurse mentioned that Ms. X.Y. paints and puts on art exhibitions. One could imagine that this provides an outlet for her creativity. In short, then, we could say that Ms. X.Y. is operating in the depressive position[2] and has adequately mourned for the life she might have had without the Crohn's disease. Thus, she can live in reality.

By contrast, Mrs. U.V. is continually asking the medical and nursing team for advice on the influence of the disease and the implications. The nature of the disease means that the staff are usually dealing with probabilities and aren't in a position to give definitive answers. For example, she has to decide when it is a good time to stop taking her Crohn's medication in order to go on with the next stage of the IVF. She continually phones and asks for advice regarding the timing. This reminds the team that the illness has deprived her of the family life she would like to have had. The nurse specialist confessed that sometimes she saw the number ringing when the phone rang and decided not to pick up the phone as she could not face talking to the patient. The nurse's guilt about the failed treatments and the patient's suffering inhibits the nursing staff from putting limits on the patient's expectations that they should be continuously available in order to listen to her symptoms and her complaints.

I don't think Mrs. U.V. can take in, or accept, the reality of her incurable chronic condition at an emotional level. Instead, she pushes her anxieties and insecurities into the nursing team, through the constant communications, lodging the responsibility and the anxiety in them. Indeed, Mrs. U.V. acts as if a hostile, intrusive, and unpredictable force was invading her life and the medical team should be protecting her from it. The difficulty the patient has letting go of her understandable wish for a cure means that she cannot accept the illness as part of *her*, or bear thinking about the implications of the illness.

Mrs. U.V. treats the medical team as if they were god-like figures, who should find a cure and stop her suffering. The phantasy of cure and the idealisation of the staff team mean that the depression about the loss of the life she cannot live because of the Crohn's is never fully faced or acknowledged. Instead, there is an endless "polite" complaint against the "experts" who either can't or won't cure the patient. This can become a cruel game as the patient continually reminds them of their shortcomings while the medical and nursing team feel persecuted by the patient's suffering, which they fail to cure. On one occasion, Mrs. U.V. contacted the nurse specialist after consultation with the medical staff to go over the doctor's

---

2 For a full account of the depressive position, see Chapter 2.

advice and approach. Apparently, in response to her questions about the medication, the doctor said he thought she could stop taking the Crohn's medication now and continue with the next stage of the IVF treatment. When the patient expressed anxieties about relapse, the doctor said that it was up to her. The nurse felt that the patient perceived this as a harsh, uncaring response and wanted to check this out with the nursing staff. The nurse explained that in order to avoid being split from the medical team she always spoke to them after a medical consultation in order to clarify the doctor's version of what was said.

I think Mrs. U.V. tries to defend herself from feelings of depression and loss regarding the painful reality of her cruel condition through projection, splitting, and denial. She splits off a distressing reality and projects it in phantasy into either the body or into someone in the external world. These are primitive psychic defences used to protect the individual's psyche from overwhelming pain and distress, characteristic of the paranoid-schizoid position.[3] The authority of the medical opinion is questioned or undermined and experienced as cruel, incompetent, or mean. But by refusing to be split, the nursing and medical team bring together the hard facts of the condition, represented by the need for diagnosis, prognosis, and treatment with care and understanding. Crohn's disease is a debilitating illness that requires a sympathetic response from staff. However, guilt induced by the condition may lead to an over-caring attitude which can create an unhelpful dependency on staff to endlessly reassure and listen to complaints about the illness. This type of relationship avoids painful facts about the reality of the illness and the limits of the medical and nursing team. It may also inhibit the development of the patient's internal capacity to own their illness and take back ownership of their lives.

Case example 3: Mourning the loss of disability in therapy

Ms. Z.A. is a woman I have seen in treatment for many years. She came into therapy in her mid-30s complaining that she had no life. She was a successful professional woman, but had no long-term relationships or interests outside of work and restricted relationships with her mother and siblings. The patient had a large congenital nevus on the side of her cheek. Her mother provided physical care, but the patient always felt her mother failed to help her come to terms with the emotional trauma involved in having an obvious physical blemish on her face. Her father died when she was young and her stepfather touched her inappropriately until she reached her teens.

My first meeting with Ms. Z.A. portrayed her lack of confidence and attitude towards her disability. She was a large woman who appeared self-conscious. She greeted me with her head twisted to one side trying to conceal one side of her face, seemed to feel shameful, and gave the impression of not wanting to make any demands on me, as if she could not quite believe that anyone would be interested

---

3 For a full account of the paranoid-schizoid position, see Chapter 2.

in her. Indeed, she confided that she sometimes imagined she was invisible and couldn't be seen. Her problem about being seen was also reflected in her voice, as she spoke in a barely audible way as though to communicate her uncertainty about her right to speak at all in her therapy session.

Ms. Z.A. believed that because she had a severe disability, she could not expect to have a normal, loving relationship. The patient mentioned that she had had numerous one-night stands with men over many years, but these always amounted to what she thought of as "sex" without love. Some months later she explained that sex often involved some form of abuse. The desire for love was painful to her as she believed it was unattainable. Thus, she explained that she tried to protect herself by putting on large amounts of weight as she believed this put her even further outside the realm of desirability. She had an internal voice that commented on her daydreams of being wanted and desired by saying, "Don't be daft, who would want you? Have you looked at yourself?"

Ms. Z.A. described herself as though she could withdraw from ownership of her body into her mind. She told me that she often cut the top of her legs with a razor. She said that she despised her body as she believed she was ugly. This gave me the impression of her having developed a cruel split between her mind and body. She also couldn't forgive her body for responding to her stepfather's inappropriate touching. Thus, she despised her body for containing desires which she felt were forbidden. Her body was also the place she located her conflicting wish to be loved and desired, on the one hand, and the hateful feelings she had for her unlovable, damaged, and ugly body, on the other. Her mind became an observation tower from which she observed and commented on this battle. This gave her a sense of being in control but at the cost of being detached from herself. She would sometimes comment on how turning away from the world of relationships in order to avoid emotional pain had cost her the chance of having a life.

Over time, the patient was able to allow herself to see and be seen and to hear and be heard. She slowly developed the idea that she could have a life of her own. However, it also involved acknowledging huge pain at the missed opportunities in her life. I sometimes thought of this pain as being represented by the weight she carried around with her. She worried her tremendous sadness would overwhelm us both in a flood of tears. She needed to be supported in experiencing feelings about the nevus and the sexual abuse and the effects these had had on her life. A change in the therapy occurred when I was able to imagine Ms. Z.A. getting on with her life, despite her disability, and could point out the way she tended to collapse into self-hatred when faced with her imperfections. I also started to take up the way she used her body to project her feelings into and then treated it with disdain as if it was a rubbish bin for psychic waste.

Case example 4: A sado-masochistic relationship with the body.

Ms. K.L. was a woman in her mid-20s with a history of severe self-harm. She was under the care of a personality disorder service and was presented to me in a supervision group by the psychiatrist who treated her. She said she was an intelligent woman who seemed to demonstrate considerable insight into her difficulties. But she admitted that she dreaded seeing Ms. K.L., as she was not sure what to say to her and often felt foolish. Ms. K.L. told the psychiatrist how an internal voice mocked her and told her to kill herself and indeed the patient often harmed herself by taking an overdose or cutting her wrists. The psychiatrist said she often felt helpless in the face of the patient's self-destructiveness and experienced withering contempt from Ms. K.L. if she expressed concern for her.

Patients who have self-harmed are sometimes referred to by staff caring for them as "manipulative" and "attention-seeking." This is understandable when staff feel drawn into situations in which they feel uncomfortable and controlled by the patient. The self-harming patient pushes responsibility for their well-being onto the mental-health professional, while attacking their own body. The psychotherapist pointed out that Ms. K.L. often talked about her body as if it was nothing to do with her and something to be treated with cruelty and contempt. In this way, she was able to project all concern about her body into the psychotherapist, leaving her free to attack her own body in a care-free and sadistic way. The psychiatrist said that she often felt her patient was watching to assess her reaction to this cruel treatment of her body. She said, "It was almost as if she was enjoying watching my reaction to her being cruel and hateful towards herself."

Rosenfeld (1971) has described the way destructive, narcissistic structures in the mind function like a pathological gang who offer a retreat from the pain of reality, by the use of an omnipotent, psychic mechanism which enables the patient to deny reality rather than face it. This destructive internal structure seduces the individual into believing that loyalty to the internal gang will protect them from all pain caused by loss, dependency, conflict, or vulnerability. Rosenfeld outlined the way parts of the internal gang promise to deal with the individual's problems in a pain-free way by employing manic defences of triumph, control, and contempt. In his paper "Who Is Killing What or Whom?" Bell (2001) highlights the way some individuals project unwanted aspects of themselves into their body which they then attack. The patient identified her body with a hateful aspect of herself, which, in a dissociated and cruel state of mind, she could attack with burning and blades.

Ms. K.L. was wedded to a powerful internal structure that dealt with the anxiety and pain of life by projecting it into her body, which she then treated with contempt. The threat of suicide, which she kept in reserve, provided the ultimate defence against psychic pain. The psychotherapist or psychiatrist or both had the feeling that if things became too difficult for her, the patient would end her life. Thus, the patient harboured a relationship with suicide and self-harm as a way of managing painful situations she felt would otherwise overwhelm her ego and lead to fragmentation or collapse.

Over time in the therapy with the psychiatrist, Ms. K.L. was able to see the cost of her attachment to the internal gang which offered her such powerful solutions to internal problems. At one point, the patient said that although she acknowledged that she was a high suicide risk and that she was in danger of killing herself, her main problem was with living. The pain of living was always threatening to overwhelm her with feelings, which she did not know how to manage, so she reverted to powerful defences that interfered with reality.

In cases like Ms. K.L.'s, the treatment aims to understand the meaning of the dissociated state and its relationship to the body. The psychiatrist provided a treatment setting where the emotional conflicts which drove the self-destructive behaviour could be explored. The patient may not be able to give up her reliance on omnipotent defences that defend her against overwhelming anxiety about the damage she has done to herself through her self-harming and to her objects in phantasy. However, the treatment can help the patient differentiate between healthy aspects of her personality and reliance on deadly, omnipotent defences that look to triumph over life.

Discussion

In this chapter I have described four patients with different relationships between their minds and their bodies and how this dynamic then affected the relationship with caring professionals. Mr. S.T. resented the referral to psychotherapy as he felt the consultant gastroenterologist was separating from the idealised god-like role assigned to him. By making a referral to the psychotherapist, the consultant was saying "I'm not a god, I have done as much as I can for your body now. I'm referring you to someone who is going to examine the influence of your mind on your body's functioning." This left him feeling betrayed, unwanted, and let down. The referral also threatened the patient's psychic equilibrium by suggesting that there was something that needed looking into in his mind and the way his mind influenced his body. He felt the consultant should go on looking for a physical solution.

In the case of the patients suffering with Crohn's disease, Ms. X.Y. could accept her disability and took the necessary steps to minimise its interference in her life. She made appropriate use of the professional support available to her. This was in contrast with Mrs. U.V. who could not accept the reality of her disability and continually demanded that the clinicians cure her of her condition. She created a malignant, dependent relationship with the professionals who were treated like reluctant gods. Medical staff were expected to provide a 24-hour reassurance service, where any problems and difficulties would be removed. The staff's guilt about the condition prevented them from putting limits on the patient's need for reassurance, although the nurse specialist did admit to feeling angry and exhausted by the patient's demands. Mrs. U.V.'s endless dependence upon external reassurance prevented her from developing her own internal resources to assess her condition, which was only managed by maintaining a malignant dependence upon the medical team. When staff failed to live up to Mrs. U.V.'s idealising expectations, the relationship changed into a sado-masochistic one where the patient subtly blamed the health-care professionals for failing to provide a cure. Mrs. U.V.'s wish for a cure to her disease, while understandable, acted as an unhelpful anti-depressant which impeded the process of mourning. Her inability to mourn the loss of a healthy body prevented her from taking a reasonable level of responsibility for her condition.

In the case of Ms. Z.A, the complaint of imperfection was directed towards herself in a self-accusatory way for being overweight and having a blemish on her face. I was left in the position of watching her while she beat herself up with her accusations of being useless, like a bystander watching a bully attack a victim.

Ms. K.L. attacked her body in a sado-masochistic way in order to avoid depressive feelings about the damage done to her in abusive relationships which she had internalised. This sado-masochistic relationship was then re-enacted in the relationship with the psychiatrist. This insight helped the mental-health professional recover from repeated re-enactments by throwing light on unhelpful patterns of relating.

I have come to think that a patient's problem in mourning their ideal self is related to their difficulty in accepting themselves as they are and/or accepting their internal objects[4] as they are or were. Instead, they hang on to an ideal of how they believe they should be and how their objects should be. Patients like this, who fail to come to terms with the reality of their situation, are always searching for an ideal figure that can cure them of their difficulties and restore them to an ideal state. When this proves impossible, they retreat into an aggrieved state against themselves, or their primary relationships, for failing to protect them from the assault of imperfections. It is as if they are saying, "It is not fair that I must bear these difficulties! Somebody *must* be to blame!" This attitude then carries over into their relationship with carers who they believe should be able to restore them to an ideal state. When they cannot, they complain that no one is looking after them. Attempts to examine the psychological elements of the caring relationship are difficult as the patient may accuse staff of neglecting to take care of their bodies, of being heartless or of contesting the serious nature of their condition.

The difficulty involved in this situation can lead to a situation where the body is given endless care, as if there is a belief that one day the magic will work and the patient will be cured! Patients sometimes believe that their endless complaints will provoke medics into undertaking medical procedures that may be unwarranted. Staff involved have difficulty separating themselves from the patient and reflecting on the reality of the clinical situation, especially when they feel they are being seen as heartless and uncaring. This relationship can be persecutory for staff as the patient continues to complain that they have failed to cure them of their symptoms. For example, I saw a patient who had an ongoing sexual relationship with a close relative. She continually presented with lower abdominal pains which eventually led to surgical investigations. One can see how the patient projected her guilt about the incestuous relationship with her relative into her genitals. She then presented the pain in her genitals to the surgeon who eventually operated, on the patient's insistence. Both the patient and the surgeon operated as if the

---

4 For a full account of what I mean by an "internal object," see Chapter 2.

patient's guilt and psychological pain could be surgically removed. The patient then accused the surgeon of operating on her unnecessarily.

Conclusion

Patients need the staff involved in caring for them to acknowledge their pain, while also being able to psychologically separate from and think about their clinical problems. This involves courage, as staff have to face their own feelings of guilt about their inadequacies and shortcomings. This enables them to separate from the futile search for either an ideal figure or someone who can produce a magical physical cure for psychological problems. Mourning allows the individual to attain an accurate assessment of themselves, including their disabilities, damaging behaviours, and shortcomings. The inability to mourn the loss of the ideal deprives the individual of the capacity to accept their shortcomings and make the necessary adaptations. With the exception of Ms. Z.A, all of the patients presented in this chapter projected psychological problems into their bodies. The relationship with their body reflected the relationship with themselves, as the body became the receptacle for unwanted parts of the self. A treatment alliance relied on an understanding of what the relationship between mind and body represented and how it impacted on the patient's relationship with health-care professionals. Trying to locate these feelings in the patient's mind rather than their bodies, thereby giving them a voice, threatened patients' habitual coping mechanisms. All these patients were trying to keep a lid on powerful feelings of sexual excitement, rage, disappointment, sadness, and guilt. It was not surprising they struggled with the process, and it should be remembered that we all need to have our defences recognised and respected, as anxieties about fragmentation may threaten to overwhelm.

References

Bell, D. (2001). Who is killing what or whom? Some notes on the internal phenomenology of suicide. *Psychoanalytic Psychotherapy, 15*(1), 21–37.

Bion, W. R. (1962). *Learning from experience*. London: Karnac Books.

Britton, R. (1989). The missing link: Parental sexuality in the Oedipus complex. In R. Britton, M. Feldman & E. O'Shaughnessy (Eds.), *The Oedipus complex today: Clinical implications* (pp. 83–101). London: Karnac Books.

Freud, S. (1923). *The ego and the id*. In *The Standard Edition of the Complete Psychological Works of Sigmund Freud*, Volume 19 (pp. 12–66). London: Hogarth Press.

Marty, P., & de M'Uzan, M. (1963). La Pensee operatoire. *Rev. Fran. Psychoanalytic, 27*(Suppl.), 1345–1346.

Rosenfeld, H. (1971). A clinical approach to the psychoanalytic theory of the life and the death instincts: An investigation of the aggressive aspects of narcissism. *International Journal of Psychoanalysis, 52*(2), 169–178.

Segal, H. (1957). Notes on symbol formation. *International Journal of Psychoanalysis, 38*(6), 391–397.

Sifneos, P. E. (1975). Problems of psychotherapy with alexithymia characteristics and physical disease. *Psychotherapy. Psychsom, 26*, 55–70.

Chapter 10

Social systems and social defence

Lord Francis was commissioned to look at why the serious problems (between January 2005 and March 2009) at Mid Staffs Foundation Trust were not identified sooner and the appropriate action taken. Lord Francis was also asked to outline what lessons could be learnt to enhance patient care. The report was delivered on 5 February 2013 and contained 290 recommendations. The key message was that the National Health Service needed to put the patient first and everything else should flow from that principle. Poor standards of care should not be tolerated and staff would be expected to speak out when they felt patient care was being compromised. Lord Francis also recommended that there should be one regulatory body and that the role of the Care Quality Commission was to be reviewed. The Francis Report outlined the way a group of staff had become systemically detached, cruel, and disengaged from their responsibilities. The report highlighted the lack of compassion from nursing staff for their patients. Since then, there has been a cacophony of cries for compassionate treatment, courses in compassion and even compassion therapy. I found myself wondering what has gone so wrong in nursing that a High Court judge has to write a report emphasising the need for compassion in nursing when this should be taken as a given!

In my role as a clinician, teacher, manager, and supervisor of nurses and other clinical staff at the Tavistock and Portman National Health Service (NHS) Foundation Trust over the past 20 years, I have been able to observe the quality of clinical engagement demonstrated across a wide range of NHS settings. I believe this has also put me in a position to assess the relationship between standards of care, the quality of training, and staff morale, as well as the management and support of front-line clinical staff.

In this chapter, I will describe a fragmented management system that fails to authorise and support clinical staff. The culture of targets and NHS Trusts' anxieties about survival have created a top-down management system that pushes anxieties about survival down the hierarchy into front-line clinical staff. This persecutory environment can undermine the thoughtful relationship between management and clinical staff which is necessary for good clinical care to thrive.

These problems have been compounded by problems in the way nurses are selected and trained. The current training still emphasises the importance of a nurse's theoretical knowledge at the expense of learning through experience. Although there have been many attempts to bridge the gap between theory and practice, many nurses continue to leave training with a deficit in their practical knowledge and/or inadequate experience of what it is to be a nurse.

In his letter to the Secretary of State, Lord Francis says:

> Building on the report of the first inquiry, the story it tells is first and foremost of appalling suffering of many patients. This was primarily caused by a serious failure on the part of a provider Trust Board. It did not listen sufficiently to its patients and staff or ensure the correction of deficiencies when these were brought to the Trust's attention.
>
> (Francis, 2013)

Proper health care has to go beyond the physical care of the patient. Crucially, it has to help patients and their relatives manage the profound anxieties associated with illness, dependency, death, and psychological disturbance. In order to provide appropriate care for their patients, staff need to feel they are supported and valued by a management structure that understands the nature of their work. They also need clinical and managerial structures that help them contain the inevitable anxieties inherent in their work. Unfortunately, in the current climate, this is not the case in parts of the NHS and as a consequence, morale is low in many areas.

There will have been specific issues and conditions in Mid Staffs NHS Trust, which are important to understand. However, many of us in the nursing profession have been concerned about the direction of travel for some time. If Mid Staffs is treated as an isolated problem, requiring special explanation, rather than an episode that reveals a chronic systemic crisis in the nursing profession, then a vital opportunity for learning will be lost. In 1999, the Tavistock and Portman ran a conference called "Facing the Crisis in Nursing." Three of the main papers presented outlined problems in the training of nurses and the fragmentation of authority in clinical areas (Evans, 2009; Fabricius, 1999; Menzies Lyth, 1999).

In this chapter, I will outline some theory I have found useful when thinking about clinical care and clinical institutions before going on to examine some of the features of the current system. I will focus on the fragmentation of the authority and support for staff in front-line clinical posts and problems in training that leave nurses without a sufficiently robust professional identity.

Theory

Klein (1946) described the healthy infant's dependence upon the mother for sustenance, care, and love in order to support the development of a strong ego and sense of self. When the infant feels safe, they feel that they are in the presence of a "good" loving mother and they have loving feelings towards her. The "good" mother is internalised by the infant in a loving way and forms the basis of the infant's ego. However, when the infant feels anxious, in pain, or neglected, they feel that they are in the presence of a "bad" threatening mother who fails to provide protection and care. Aggressive feelings towards this uncaring "bad" figure then further threaten the infant's ego and sense of security. In order to protect the ego and any residual good feeling, the infant projects these aggressive feelings towards the "bad" mother out into the external world. These aggressive feelings are then felt to reside outside the object in the external world and are always threatening to return. Klein described this as the *paranoid-schizoid position* and psychic defences in this scenario are based on primitive mental mechanisms such as splitting, projection, denial, and idealisation.

Over time, the infant begins to lessen the split between the "good" mother they love and the "bad" mother they hate. Indeed, the infant starts to recognise that their aggressive and loving feelings are both directed towards the same mother. This causes feelings of depression and guilt as the infant is faced with the anxiety of realising that they may have aggressive impulses towards the same mother they depend upon for sustenance and life. Good objects that have been attacked or damaged form part of the internal world. Klein called this state of mind the *depressive position* and it may lead some people to pursue an adult career based on reparation, such as nursing or medicine. Klein also recognised that guilt and depression can lead to a regression into a manic state of mind in which the infant tries to deny their dependence upon the object by denigrating the object and employing mechanisms of triumph.

Bion (1962) developed this theory further by outlining what he described as the relationship between *container and the contained*. He outlined the way the infant's ego is overwhelmed by raw psychic experiences that are unavailable for thought. Bion outlined the way the infant evacuates and communicates these raw experiences through noises, looks, and bodily movements. The mother takes in these raw experiences before using her capacity to empathise and think about the infant's state of mind. Bion described this as the mother's capacity for *reverie*. In order for this process to work, the mother needs to be able to be affected by the baby's communication without being overwhelmed by it. Thus, the mother's ability to "contain" the infant's raw emotions helps turn raw emotional experience into "food for thought." In addition to taking in the communication, the infant takes in the feeling that they are being cared for by a figure that understands their feelings.

Segal (1957, 1991) also built on these ideas by describing the difference between a symbolic representation and a symbolic equation. In the case of a symbolic representation, there is an acknowledgement of the difference between the symbol and the object being symbolised. However, in the case of a *symbolic equation*, there is no differentiation between the object and symbol. In a symbolic equation, there is a complete identity between the object and the symbol. This gives rise to what we mean by concrete thinking—using words as if they were the thing itself. Thus, in a symbolic equation, the statement "give me a minute" is literally interpreted as 60 seconds, rather than the symbolic representation of the idea which is, "give me some time." In order to maintain the difference between a symbolic equation and symbolic representation, the subject needs to be supported in establishing a psychic separation from the concrete object.

Britton (1989) describes the importance of the Oedipal situation in supporting thought and the development of symbolic thinking. He emphasised the importance of the third object (psychically, the father) in supporting the mother-infant couple, while also providing room for separation and thought. The triangular situation provides a structure for thinking and helps prevent the collapse into concrete thinking or enactments.

Jacques (1955) applied the theories developed above to social systems. He developed a theory for describing the way individuals within a social system act together in order to produce a defensive social structure that defends its members from anxiety. In her seminal paper "Social Systems as a Defence against Anxiety," Menzies Lyth (1959) applied Jacques's theory to a hospital setting in which an unhealthy defensive social system had developed. While it is necessary to have defences against anxiety, problems arise when primitive defences of splitting, projection, and denial take over and adversely affect individuals' and teams' capacities to deal with the anxieties in a more mature way. Menzies Lyth outlined the way the social system unwittingly developed a rigid and primitive defensive system designed to distance the nurse from the patients' suffering. This was accompanied by a process of dehumanising the contact between the nurse and patient, resulting in the patient being viewed as a medical condition rather than a human being with feelings. Anxiety generated from the nurses' contact with patients and their suffering was then projected into concrete rituals, which functioned like an obsessive-compulsive defence against contamination.

The therapeutic setting

Implicit in the role of the nurse's relationship with the patient is the capacity to empathise and contain the patient's suffering. This involves a process of taking in the patient's state of mind and projections through observations and contact with the patient's emotional and physical state (Fabricius, 1991). Using his/her own internal experience of suffering and anxieties about illness and damage, the nurse forms an identification with the patient. He/she conveys understanding of the patient's anxiety and pain through a compassionate and thoughtful attitude. This is conveyed by his/her manner in carrying out clinical tasks. Thus, the nurse contains the patient's emotional states in the same way Bion described the mother doing for her baby.

When things are going well, this identification with the patient is based on the patient being a symbolic representative of the nurse's own damaged objects, but not wholly identified with them in a concrete way. A separation "is maintained between the patient's state of mind and damaged figures from the nurse's internal world" (Segal, 1957). The capacity to move between empathic identification for the patient's suffering and objective professionalism is an essential process in maintaining a mature and healthy clinical approach. However, this process requires the nurse to take in and "contain" the patient's pain, vulnerability, and anxiety without being overwhelmed by them. If the nurse is overwhelmed, there is a danger of an unbalanced symbolic equation developing at the level of the nurse's unconscious phantasy which means he/she can no longer distinguish their own internal damaged objects from the patient they are nursing. This is much less likely to happen when support is provided to the nurse by management structures, such as clinical discussion, reflective practice, and good management. On the one hand, these opportunities help the nurse separate from the effect of the patient and restores their capacity to take an objective clinical approach, while on the other hand, staff who have become hardened to patients' projections can be helped to reflect more on the emotional impact of the clinical contact. These organisational structures act like Bion's maternal reverie and support the nurse first by containing them, which then permits them to separate from identifications with patients and reflect upon them by thinking about them much as the father can help the mother separate from the mother-baby merger in Britton's triangular position (see above). Thus, reflective practice in particular is key in helping the nurse maintain the difference between the patient as a symbolic representation of damaged figures in the nurse's internal world.

When the nurse loses the capacity to separate his/her personal anxieties, thus forming a symbolic equation in which the patient becomes concretely identified with his/her own damaged objects, confusion arises. This confusion of the internal world with the external world can lead to either manic and/or heroic attempts on behalf of the nurse to cure the patient, followed by a sense of despair at the impossibility of their task. The nurse may develop a hard external skin that gives the impression of cruel indifference as a way of keeping the patient and his/her difficulties at a distance. This is why time and resources for reflection on the clinical work should be seen not as a luxury but rather as an essential part of good clinical (and nursing) practice. Research demonstrates that well-led and well-managed teams use these structures as opportunities to examine and think about their clinical practice.

Teams that treat patients whose clinical condition is accompanied by disturbing psychological states of mind often need the help of an external supervisor. For example, patients in mental health settings with a diagnosis of EUPD (Emotionally Unstable Personality Disorder) often get under the skin of staff, while those with a diagnosis of ASPD (Anti-Social Personality Disorder) can induce sadistic responses from staff. These patient groups can have a profound impact upon staff and can undermine the team's capacity to contain patients. Clinical supervision from an external supervisor, who acts as a third object in the way described by Britton, can help to restore the container. By acting as the third point in the nurse-patient-supervisor triangle, the supervisor can provide an appropriate space for thinking about the psychological impact of the work and reduce the pull towards re-enactments (Evans, 2011).

Leadership and institutional support

The nurse-patient relationship takes place within a clinical team structure, which can help to contain the anxieties inherent in clinical work. The team contains individual's work with patients by providing a clear structure that supports this task. Good leadership is an essential ingredient in any well-run team as the leader is responsible for establishing an environment in which high-quality clinical care can take place. This leadership provides teams with clear lines of accountability, realistic goals, effective communication, high standards in relation to recruitment of staff, appropriate training, adequate staffing levels, and good relationships with ancillary support. The team's capacity to provide good care is also affected by many factors outside the ward or team, including the quality of managerial support and containment provided by senior clinical managers external to the ward or team. Teams need senior clinical managers who are engaged in helping them to resolve the conflicts and dilemmas involved in managing difficult clinical issues. Senior clinical managers also need to help clinical managers review staff performance and support them with issues concerning recruitment and development. In this scenario, it is the senior clinical manager who can act as a third object to help the ward manager restore his/her capacity to contain the front-line team.

A study from history

In 1959, Isabel Menzies Lyth, a British psychoanalyst, was invited to King's College in London in order to examine a problem in relation to the allocation of trainees within the hospital. She decided to look upon the problems she encountered as symptoms of underlying difficulties within the institution. At the time of the study (1959), the Matron was ultimately responsible for the running of the hospital as a clinical service, and she had extensive authority over all clinical matters, from standards of care to cleaning, catering, laundry supplies, etc. This kind of authority was also reflected throughout the hospital, so, in turn, the charge nurse, or Ward Sister as they were called at that time, was responsible for all aspects of ward life, including who came onto the ward and for what purpose. The Matron and the Nursing Officers who supported her would "walk the wards" on a daily basis. This maintained a personal and ongoing link between the wider hospital management system and each individual clinical area. Thus, Ward Sisters were able to talk to the Matron and her senior nursing management on a daily basis about the clinical situation on the ward. The managerial relationship was designed to address ongoing problems as well as to help with handling immediate crises. The Matron of the hospital was also responsible for the School of Nursing and so her dual role embodied the organic relationship between clinical practice and training.

Although this system had many positive attributes, there were also negative aspects, which undermined the benefits of this integrated system. In her paper, Menzies Lyth outlined the way the system encouraged an over-reliance on

Nursing Officers and the Matron to make decisions. She described an obsessional institutional defence, which involved pushing responsibility for decisions up the hierarchy in unnecessary and risk-averse ways, which undermined the decision-making capacity at the ward level. Thus, legitimate and necessary anxiety associated with the management of the clinical area and the standard of clinical care was projected away from the clinical setting, creating a passive dependent relationship between the Ward Sister and the Matron. This system encouraged the projection of capacity and ability up the hierarchy into the Matron while incompetence and lack of trust were projected down the hierarchy into the Ward Sisters. This system undermined the Ward Sisters' confidence in their ability to do their work and contain their clinical area. It was as if rather than supporting the function of the Ward Sister, the Matron was operating as a destructive "third object," who undermined the Ward Sisters' confidence, and therefore the containing function of the wards.

The fragmentation of authority

The clear lines of accountability and integration that are necessary for good morale and good team functioning have been eroded away over time in the NHS.

In the late 1960s, as a result of the negative aspects of the system, the authority of the Matron was removed. In addition, the managers further up the hierarchy have removed authority from senior clinical managers, formerly the Matron and her team, for many important areas of care such as cleaning, catering, and laundry in order to reduce costs. These changes have had their own negative consequences as they have weakened the clinical nurse managers' control over key areas of the setting. Also, the responsibility for training has been removed from the clinical area and now resides with the universities. Clinical nurse managers are left with the responsibility and anxieties about the quality of care available in the clinical setting, but without much of the authority they need in order to execute these responsibilities to the best of their ability.

Consequently, many nurses are reluctant to take positions of authority and prefer to stay on the nursing bank and/or work as an agency nurse. It is my experience that many nursing staff do not feel they have either the necessary authority or the required support from those in senior management roles to manage effectively.

Assumptions that monitoring, performance management or intervention was the responsibility of someone else (Francis, 2013). Nurses feel that the containing structures are no longer there and the management is seen as distant and persecutory rather than supportive and helpful. The vacuum in clinical leadership was recognised in the early 1980s with the introduction of Nurse Development Units, but these did not survive the managerial changes of the late 1980s. The new style Modern Matron in 2000 was tasked with arresting the falling standards of clinical care.

However, the problems are systemic and so cannot be solved by the re-introduction of a post that bears the name ("Modern Matron") but lacks the authority and wide-ranging responsibility that characterised the old-style Matron. It is like trying to reinvent the wheel but providing no road for it to run on, and serious concerns about standards of cleanliness and the quality of food provided in hospitals remain. Hence, the lack of clear lines of accountability and authority presents an ongoing problem: *A culture focused on doing the system's business—not that of the patients* (Francis, 2013).

The system that manages the NHS is driven by a belief that competition and targets drive up quality and provide the best guarantee of getting value for money for the taxpayer. It is widely known that only strong NHS Trusts will survive in this new market and failing trusts will be taken over. The three main sources of survival anxiety are the internal market, austerity measures, and targets.

The internal market

The internal market introduced early in the 1990s has created an increasingly fragmented health care system as different parts of the system are encouraged to compete for patient contracts, rather than work together in the interests of the patient. Competition can be seen as healthy and representing an important source of motivation for improvement and progress. However, unhealthy aspects of competition may also affect relationships between colleagues or services when destructive rivalry based on triumph and survival starts to infect thinking.

The market is always in danger of disintegrating into a fragmented world in which there is an attempt to deny the interdependence between individuals, disciplines, and clinical areas. Manic defences are employed in order to triumph over feelings of vulnerability, inadequacy, and failure. These states of mind are then projected around the social system. The world starts to be divided between survivors and casualties, winners and losers: splitting reminiscent of the good (ideal) and bad (denigrated) of the paranoid-schizoid position (see the "Theory" section of this chapter). This superior and defensive state of mind undermines the attitude required for reverie and learning through experience. In a paper titled "Primitive Mind of State," Bell (1996) outlined the way the "market" is seen to represent a system free of waste, efficient, and lean, where only the fittest survive. In reality, market forces in health care systems often appeal to the parts of the personality that wish to triumph over feelings of inadequacy, vulnerability, and/or dependency.

The introduction of payment by results has seen the introduction of a tool for evaluating the level of the patient's difficulties and accompanying packages of care appropriate to the patient's needs. A price for the package of care is then identified and commissioners pay for a certain number of packages. This system encourages management to think of the patient as suffering from a condition which will be dealt with by the appropriate package of care for an identifiable length of time. Patients with long-term, complex needs requiring interventions from different parts of the health or social care system pose a particular problem for this "package of care" system. Long-term care is expensive; this group of patients has the additional burden of having to fight their way through layers of regulation and red tape in order to get the care they need. Services have lists of eligibility and exclusion criteria, designed to protect them from expensive or demanding cases where patients have complex or long-term clinical conditions. This is pertinent in relation to mental health care where many services view the patient as someone who suffers from a list of symptoms that need to be removed rather than a person with a particular psychological structure and personality. Increasingly common-place is the "provision" of short treatment programmes that may be temporarily helpful but bear no relationship to the long-term and complex nature of patients' clinical conditions. Consequently, patients are often passed from one service to another, as they search for a service that will look at the long-term nature of their difficulties.

Austerity measures

> The report has identified numerous warning signs which cumulatively, or in some cases singly, could and should have alerted the system to the problems developing at the Trust.
>
> (Francis, 2013)

As financial constraints have increased, economic pressure has forced a down-grading of clinical staff and of the skill mix required by the team. Nurses fre-quently have to re-apply for their jobs, and then accept lower salaries when they are re-appointed, so consequently, large numbers of experienced staff have taken either voluntary redundancy or retirement. These changes also mean that health-care assistants are increasingly left on the front line of clinical care while quali-fied nurses become more and more responsible for management. Morale amongst nurses is at an all-time low in many areas as experienced staff retire early. Forensic mental health staff working in a high-secure setting recently informed me that they were only allowed one qualified member of staff for each ward at night. A change in shift patterns in many areas means that nurses are already work-ing 12-hour shifts with very little handover time. The loss of this overlap time between shifts is a serious threat to the crucial teaching sessions, supervisions, or reflective practice groups, which are an essential part of ongoing clinical practice and should not be perceived as a luxury (Evans, 2007).

These changes can make front-line staff feel as if they are on a treadmill, with very little respite. They may develop an unexpressed resentment of both the organisation and the patients they care for, as they are going uncared for themselves. It should be no surprise that "burn out" and clinical "mistakes" are on the increase. However, such failures are too often blamed on the individual, with nurses being referred for stress counselling, thereby diverting attention from the systemic causes. In this anxiety-fuelled environment, it is common-place for clinical staff to develop defensive practices designed to avoid criticism rather than to care for and therefore treat the patient. Staff are also frightened to speak out.

> An institutional culture which ascribed more weight to positive information about the service than to information capable of implying cause for concern.
>
> (Francis, 2013)

Financial pressures and the demands of a target culture mean that senior managers are often unable to really listen to concerns about lack of resources for patient care. Clinical managers who are responsible for meeting their targets and staying within their budget may be tempted to stop co-operating with neighbouring services by sharing resources as they become preoccupied with the financial health of their own area. Once again, this paranoid-schizoid state of mind undermines the need for services and staff in different areas to work together in the interest of their patients.

The target culture

> Failure was in part the consequence of allowing a focus on reaching national access targets, achieving financial balance and seeking foundation trust status to at the cost of delivering acceptable standards of care.
>
> (Francis, 2013)

Over the past 20 years, there has been a substantial shift in the clinician-patient relationship and the authority of the clinician is no longer accepted as a guarantee of good quality care. Instead, NHS regulatory authorities, commissioners and patients look for "objective measurable outcomes" to provide an assurance of quality and good care. The information gathered can be helpful as it may provide objective information about one aspect of the system's functioning. But the information provided needs to be fed into the managerial system in a way which adds to the overall picture. Then, the senior clinical manager in conjunction with the clinical nurse manager can think about the meaning of the information and decide on appropriate action.

However, information often comes back to the clinical nurse manager in the form of an anxious directive: "Your service is failing to hit this target and you need to improve this area of performance." This sort of directive has the impact of an instruction from an authority external to the ward that overrides any local authority or requirement to think about either the meaning of the figures or the priorities of the local situation. I have also noticed that the communication sometimes contains a moralistic tone: "Aren't you interested in improving the service to your patients?" or "Don't you care about the Trust's monitor rating?" In these communications, which are designed to induce guilt, there is no recognition of inadequate staffing levels or front-line clinical realities. This form of communication can increase the clinical nurse manager's feeling that people outside the immediate clinical area and at some distance from the clinical area are eroding his/her appropriate sense of authority and control. It is also in danger of causing a paranoid-schizoid split between front-line clinical staff and managers external to the clinical area.

> In introducing the first report, I said that it should be patients—not numbers—which counted. That remains my view.
>
> (Francis, 2013)

> Although objective measures can be helpful, they provide no more guarantee of good treatment than the clinician's opinion. Our preoccupation with measuring everything can become a defensive distraction from the task of caring for the patient.
>
> (Proctor, Wallbank, and Dhaliwal, 2013).

The fear of failing to hit the various targets set by the Care Quality Commission, Monitor, NHS Litigation Authority, and Care Commissioning Groups, and failing to maintain a balanced budget does persecute NHS Trusts. Responsibility for targets is located with the senior managers running central services such as Human Resources, Clinical Governance, Risk Management, Contracts, and Information Governance. The senior managers running these departments are accountable for overseeing the NHS Trust's performance against targets, and there are real financial penalties that may threaten a Trust's future if the required standards are not met. Performance is measured against a series of targets monitoring different aspects of the Trust's work. Thus, the clinical area is required to provide figures and information that contribute towards reports on patient turnover, length of stay, the number of patient complaints, performance against clinical contracts, patient satisfaction, ward cleanliness, standards of information governance, staff sickness, outcome monitoring data, disability data, ethnicity data, case note standards, payment by results figures, outcome measures, mandatory staff training, and many others. The risk of failing to reach a target provokes a directive (often by email) demanding an increased effort in the area concerned. Senior managers from these various Trust Departments emphasise the importance of their own targets, and anxiety is often conveyed through the tone of the communication, which takes no account of the clinical team's capacity to meet the target in question. Pressure builds as the demand for immediate action and resolution of a specific problem often ignores the fact that the clinical nurse manager and his/her staff have to continue running the entire service effectively so that patients are receiving the attention they require. The clinical team's resources are pulled in different directions as the clinical nurse manager tries to meet the demand to meet targets from different parts of the managerial system. Thus, staff teams are exposed to unrealistic expectations, which have a damaging effect on morale.

This sort of environment also increases the likelihood of clinical priorities becoming secondary to the needs of the institution to achieve targets in an attempt to deal with its survival anxieties. Perverse outcomes often arise when this happens, a case of the tail wagging the dog. For example, Accident & Emergency departments are under immense pressure to see patients within certain time constraints and there are financial penalties for the Trust if they fail to meet these targets. This pressure can result in patients either being admitted to inappropriate wards or even being sent home when in reality they need admitting. The danger is that the target culture encourages a "blame game" where no one wants to be left holding responsibility for the failure to hit the target. You can sometimes see in the email trail in which half the Trust is copied how individuals deny responsibility and push the blame elsewhere. Thus, targets have the unwitting effect of undermining the most precious resource of all in the NHS—that of clinical judgement.

In a recent paper reviewing "Social Systems as a Defence against Anxiety," William Halton outlined the similarity between the defensive structure outlined by Menzies Lyth and obsessive defences designed to keep the patient and his/her anxiety at a distance (Halton, 2013). When Menzies Lyth did her study at King's College, the primary concern was for patient care. By contrast, the current system is confronted by two anxieties coming from different directions. Up from the clinical work come the anxieties related to fears of managing illness, psychological disturbance, and dying, while down from the management come institutional anxieties about survival. There is a danger that this system creates a split between management and front-line clinical staff. Far from the system containing front-line staff, there is a tendency for management to push their anxieties into front-line staff via shards of survival anxiety. The danger is that this leaves clinical staff feeling blamed, overwhelmed, and unsupported. This in turn can lead to loss of morale and poor patient care as clinical staff feel that they are constantly failing on all fronts. Revans (1959) showed that there was a direct link between the morale of nursing teams and patient recovery. The split can also mean that misunderstanding abounds as management, filled with their own anxieties about survival, turn a deaf ear to clinical staff's concerns. The primary purpose of targets has been subverted from the improvement of patient care to the survival of the hospital or clinical unit.

The effect of the survival anxiety on the healthcare system resulting from the internal market, financial cuts, and targets is that senior management are so anxious and insecure that they are not able to provide the containment and "reverie" that clinical managers need. The resulting lack of empathy from senior managers for clinical staff is one of the factors that lead to nurses' lack of empathy for patients.

The training of nurses

> The complaints heard at both the first inquiry and this one testified not only to inadequate staffing levels, but poor leadership, recruitment and training.
>
> (Francis, 2013)

Nurse training institutions have the task of helping their trainees develop their professional identity in addition to academic knowledge and technical ability. This identity is developed through contact with the good role models they encounter on clinical placements. Over time, the student can internalise the qualities of these role models by working alongside senior clinical colleagues on clinical placements. As mentioned in the opening paragraphs of this chapter, trainees must be receptive to their patient's psychological state, whilst also being able to separate themselves from their patients' anxieties in order to maintain professional objectivity. Menzies Lyth outlined the way patients and their relatives transmit their anxieties about illness—and furthermore, mortality—to the nursing staff. The staff need to manage their own fears around this, as well as any feelings of disgust and vulnerability related to their patients' physical and psychological condition. The social system surrounding the nurses therefore must support both the individual nurses and the clinical managing team as a whole to achieve this.

As previously discussed in her 1959 study, Menzies Lyth described the way the social system within a training hospital created a defensive social system that fragmented the nurse-patient relationship and turned the patient into a diagnosis rather than a fellow human. This was done through a process of fragmenting the nurse-patient contact into task-orientated nursing, for example, Nurse A takes the patient's temperature; Nurse B makes the bed. Nurses would also refer to patients using diagnostic terms—"the liver in bed number 25"—in an attempt to distance themselves from the patient as a person. This fragmentation meant that patients were deprived of a nurse who related to them as a whole human being and empathised with them. You can't empathise with "a liver." There was no practice of individual supervision for nurses and they were not helped to deal with the emotional impact of their work. Nurses were also treated like objects with no individual characteristics or feelings of their own, e.g. Nurse A is sent to surgical and Nurse B to medical with no thought about their individual skills, knowledge, or ability to complete the task. This undermines the crucial element of identifying and acknowledging a nurse's individual interests and abilities—knowing the nurse "as a whole person" too.

By the 1990s, Project 2000 was introduced. This represented shift from the apprenticeship-based model of training in hospitals to a university-based higher education award. The change moved responsibility for nurse training from the Schools of Nursing, which were attached to the hospitals, to the universities. Accompanying this physical move was a shift in the centre of gravity from the "hands-on" learning of the apprenticeship model to academic learning in the classroom. There was also a shift in emphasis in student nurse selection from an aptitude for the vocation of nursing to a preoccupation with academic ability.

In the current model, trainees are often supernumerary and spend time observing clinical practice or attending clinical placements for short periods of time. Hard-pressed staff are sometimes reluctant to invest time in transient students who are not part of the clinical numbers. Crucially, it is the quality of engagement between the student nurse and the clinical team that supports the student nurse's identification with clinical colleagues. If the student is committed to the clinical team, she will receive commitment in return. If the involvement with the team is half-hearted or fragmented, the student will not get the support or engagement from the clinical team she needs in order to learn (Evans, 2009). What is more, nurse tutors once used to support placements by visiting the clinical placement regularly and holding teaching sessions on the ward, observing and assessing clinical practice. This made the link tutor a crucial person for supporting the student nurse's ability to manage the emotional demands of direct patient contact. In another paper titled "Psychoanalytic Understanding and Nursing: A Supervisory Workshop with Nurse Tutors," Fabricius (1995) described her experience of running supervisory groups for student nurses, which aimed to help them digest and then learn from their experiences in clinical placements. This approach helps the student face painful aspects of the work as well as developing the self-critical objectivity necessary for high-quality clinical practice.

The "evidence base" and theory behind medicine and nursing provide a vital pillar of clinical training. However, I believe we threw the "baby out with the bathwater" when Project 2000 was introduced by widening the gap that already existed between theory and practice; and despite numerous attempts this gap has yet to be bridged (Hewison and Wildman, 1996). In her paper, "Running on the Spot or Can Nursing Really Change?," Fabricius (1991) outlined her belief that the movement from the emotionally charged experience of "hands-on" nursing, which involved being with the patient, to the academic and abstract environment of the classroom represented a wish to retreat from the disturbing aspects of physical and emotional contact with a patient who is ill or dying. Fabricius argued that this represented an attack on the nurse's maternal function and would ultimately undermine the nurse's identity as a caring figure from which he/she derives so much professional authority.

Financial pressure on universities has meant that many university link tutors are trying to oversee too many students and cannot give either the necessary tutorial time or make the regular hospital visits to support students in their clinical placements in a meaningful way (Department of Health [DH], 2006). A weak or distant relationship between the tutor and the student can mean that the student drifts or fails to make proper use of the experience gained during training. Lack of time visiting clinical placements means that qualified staff working on these wards do not get a chance to discuss the student nurse with the tutor. Thus, clinical staff, tutors, and students struggle to find the time necessary to triangulate their picture of the individual's development. A recent report suggested that there was an ambiguity in the current system regarding who is responsible for failing student nurses who persistently fall short of acceptable standards. This means that some students who have been identified as having persistent problems in attitude and/or ability often continue on into their third year and beyond, despite the fact that there are ongoing questions about their level of functioning. Once again, the defensive nature of the system creates a fragmented social structure that breaks up the relationships necessary to support development.

As a consequence of the failings in this system, many nurse directors and managers have recognised that recently qualified staff are often unable to complete basic nursing procedures (Department of Health, 2006). An additional problem is that many universities have had contracts (with financial targets attached) to fill a certain number of student nurse places. As a consequence, the quality and aptitude of students recruited may have been less of a priority than the contractual need to fill training places.

We need to ensure that student nurses are interested in caring for people as the first and foremost priority and therefore we should shift the centre of gravity for training back to the clinical settings. Nursing students learn best practice from working alongside qualified nurses in live clinical situations. All clinical areas are potentially learning environments and the teaching function of clinical areas needs to be supported. This system, in turn, needs to be supported by nurse tutors who have the time to genuinely support the students in learning through their experience. In this way, the trainee nurse's capacity for empathy can be supported, monitored, and developed in situ.

Discussion

Things have never been perfect in the healthcare system and ideas of a "golden age" are in themselves defensive and represent a denial of reality. Defences against psychic pain and anxiety are ubiquitous, universal, and necessary. However, there are significant differences between primitive defences designed to avoid reality and more mature psychological defences. In the current structure, we have supplanted the rather obsessive institutional defence of the 1950s and 1960s for an even more primitive defensive structure. This defensive structure has to deal with a double whammy—the patient's anxieties about illness, death, and fragmentation, on the one hand, and the Trust's or clinical service's concerns about survival, on the other. Anxiety and blame are pushed around the system like a pinball bouncing back and forth between the different areas of responsibility. This is reminiscent of defences that emanate from the paranoid-schizoid position as the institution employs splitting, projection, denial, idealisation, denigration, and manic triumph. Meanwhile, there has been an erosion of the sorts of structures and relationships that help contain anxiety.

The squeeze on the time available for teaching supervision and/or case discussion undermines the time and structures necessary to support the reflective capacity of individuals and teams. Hence, the structures that support the clinician's capacity to digest experience have been removed in an attempt to reduce costs. Instead, we are creating a system that increasingly distances the patient and his/her suffering from the nurse. There is also a danger that this system undermines the authority of the clinical nurse manager for the clinical setting. Survival anxiety can create a split between front-line clinical managers who have the responsibility of managing resources in their clinical area and the managers of the NHS Trust who carry responsibility for targets. The target culture and regulatory system also dictate that much authority is externally outsourced for example, catering, cleaning, security, etc., from the clinical nurse manager.

Clinical leadership roles are vital containers of anxiety within the healthcare system. However, anxieties about survival and fear of persecution can erode the confidence and authority of the clinical nurse manager. Clinical nurse managers are also often left on their own with anxieties about how they are going to manage the gap between senior managerial expectations and the capacity of their unit to deliver the clinical standards necessary. The persecutory environment increases the sense of the clinical area being policed by a raft of senior managers rather than supported by senior management colleagues who understand what it takes to manage a clinical area. When this happens, it undermines the important function that senior managers can have in acting as the third object that helps clinical nurse managers think through the conflicts, difficulties, and anxieties that need to be managed in their clinical area.

Over 50 years ago, Menzies Lyth was invited to consult on a failing hospital system. However, we still have not learnt the lessons Menzies Lyth outlined in her paper. Clinical nursing staff need to be supported by an authoritative managerial and clinical structure, which helps the nurse bear the anxieties inherent in the work. In order to achieve this, it is essential that clinical nursing and medical authority are at the heart of the managerial system. Menzies Lyth (1999) emphasised her belief that the most effective form of staff support was provided by good clinical managers. She also outlined the need for clinical areas to be managed by authoritative figures who are empowered to take full responsibility for the quality of clinical care provided to their patients. Whilst financial constraints represent important realities about finite resources, their influence has to be balanced against authority derived from clinical realities about care and treatment. Clinical services need experienced staff who are familiar with the realities of clinical practice and have the necessary authority and experience to know when corners are being cut, standards are being compromised, and/or risks are being taken in a way which will negatively impact patient care.

Teams also need senior clinical managers who assist them in their difficult job via regular and supportive contact, rather than directives and surveillance. Senior managers also need to have the authority and confidence to communicate difficulties back up the hierarchy, as well as communicating important issues down the hierarchy and being prepared to stand up to senior colleagues in order to protect standards of care in front-line services.

Central to the Francis Report is the conclusion that the patient and clinical voice were not being heard and it appears that six years on, little has changed. The current top-down management system, driven by a target-based and finance-orientated culture, has a tendency to push clinical staff's concerns down the hierarchy and away from the upper tiers of management (Cunnane and Warwick, 2013). The voice that carries knowledge about the effect of cuts and expresses anxiety about patient care is often treated as if it is the carrier of a disease and needs to be barrier-nursed. In reality, it is often the voice of experience, and for our healthcare system to thrive, it needs to be listened to.

Conclusion

All healthcare systems have problems. These are, by their nature, multifaceted. However, when the problems outlined here are combined with the current austerity measures, the scene is set for the eruption of more toxic situations such as those exposed at Mid Staffs. It is surprising that similar events are not reported more often. However, listening to nurses present their clinical work has convinced me that, despite the system's tendency towards fragmentation and the lack of support for front-line clinical staff, there are still large numbers of nurses who remain extremely committed to their patients and endeavour to do the best they can within the existing system. My worry is that we have reached a tipping point and can no longer rely on individuals' valency towards care and responsibility.

The persecution inherent in the system is creating an environment which is antithetical to thoughtful care. The consequence is that only exceptional clinical managers can juggle the demands between the persecution of the "target culture" while keeping the care of the patients at the heart of their thinking. This is not a sustainable position. In theatres that deal with matters of "life and death," you need leaders with experience who can manage the anxieties in the work and can support their front-line staff. These clinical leaders, in turn, need support from senior managers who can help front-line clinical managers contain anxiety and reduce the temptation towards blame, fragmentation, and splitting.

As Lord Francis said in his report, we need to put the clinical care and nurturing of our patients back at the heart of the NHS. In order to do so, we need to start addressing the current moralistic and persecutory culture of the current NHS. Exhorting nursing staff to work harder, be more empathic, and feel guilty for shortcomings in clinical services while depriving them of adequate training, managerial support, time to learn, or status within the system is a recipe for disaster. The NHS needs to establish a clinical training system that supports trainees through apprenticeship training, repairs damage done to the authority of nurses and nursing in the system, and develops structures that really support and listen to staff.

References

Bell, D. (1996). Primitive mind of state. *Psychoanalytic Psychotherapy, 10*(1), 45–57.

Bion, W. (1962). A theory of thinking. *International Journal of Psychoanalysis, 43,* 306–310.

Britton, R. (1989). The missing link: Parental sexuality in the Oedipus complex. In R. Britton, M. Feldman & E. O'Shaughnessy (Eds.), *The Oedipus complex today: Clinical implications* (pp. 83–101). London: Karnac Books.

Cunnane, D., & Warwick, R. (2013, February 14). *Francis report: What went wrong with NHS leadership? Guardian professional.* https://www.theguardian.com/healthcare-network/2013/feb/14/francis-report-nhs-leadership.

Department of Health (D.H.). (2006). *From values to action: The chief nursing officer's review of mental health nursing.* London: Author.

Evans, M. (2007). Being driven mad: Towards understanding borderline and other disturbed states of mind through the use of the counter transference. *Psychoanalytic Psychotherapy*, *21*(3), 216–232.

Evans, M. (2009). Tackling the theory–practice gap in mental health nurse training. *Mental Health Practice*, *13*(2), 21–24.

Evans, M. (2011). Pinned against the ropes; Understanding anti-social personality disordered patients through use of the counter transference. *Psychoanalytic Psychotherapy*, *25*(2), 143–156.

Fabricius, J. (1991). Running on the spot or can nursing really change? *Psychoanalytic Psychotherapy*, *5*(2), 97–108.

Fabricius, J. (1995). Psychoanalytic understanding and nursing: A supervisory workshop with nurse tutors. *Psychoanalytic Psychotherapy*, *9*(1), 17–29.

Fabricius, J. (1999). Reflections on the crisis in nursing. *Psychoanalytic Psychotherapy*, *13*(3), 203–206.

Francis, R. (2013). *The mid Staffordshire NHS foundation trust public inquiry*. Chaired by Robert Francis QC HC 947. Report of the Mid Staffordshire NHS Foundation Trust Public Inquiry Executive Conclusion. London: The Stationery Office.

Halton, W. (2013). Obsessional-punitive defences in care systems: Menzies Lyth revisited. Unpublished manuscript.

Hewison, A., & Wildman, S. (1996). The theory–practice gap in nursing: A new dimension. *Journal of Advanced Nursing*, *244*(4), 754–761.

Jacques, E. (1955). Social systems as a defence against persecutory and depressive anxiety. In M. Klein, P. Heimann & R. Money-Kyrle (Eds.), *New directions in psychoanalysis* (pp. 478–498). London: Tavistock Publications.

Klein, M. (1946). Notes on some schizoid mechanisms. *International Journal of Psychoanalysis*, *27*(3–4), 99–110.

Menzies Lyth, I. (1959). The functioning of social systems as a defence against anxiety. Reprinted (1988) In *Containing anxiety in institutions* (Vols. 1 and 2, pp. 43–85). London: Free Association Books.

Menzies Lyth, I. (1999). Facing the crisis. *Psychoanalytic Psychotherapy*, *13*(3), 207–212.

Proctor, S., Wallbank, S., & Dhaliwal, J. (2013, February 28). What compassionate care means. *Health Service Journal*. https://www.hsj.co.uk/comment/what-compassionate-care-means/5055438.article.

Revans, R. (1959, September). The hospital as an organism: A study in communication and morale. *Preprint no. 7 of a paper presented at the sixth international meeting of the Institute of Management Science*. Paris: Pergamon.

Segal, H. (1957). Notes on symbol formation. *International Journal of Psychoanalysis*, *38*(6), 391–397.

Segal, H. (1991). *Dream, phantasy and art*. London/New York, NY: Tavistock Publications/ Routledge.

Index

actuarial risk profiles 51
alexithymia 107
alpha elements 109
analyst-centred interpretations 79
anti-psychotic medication 3
Anti-Social Personality Disorder (ASPD) 125
anxiety 37; survival anxiety 135
ASPD (Anti-Social Personality Disorder) 125
assessment of suicidal risk 50–1
attempts at eradicating psychosis 29–30
austerity measures 129–30
authority: fragmentation of 127–8; historical examples 126–7

bad mother 11–12, 16, 123
Bell, D. 128–9
beta elements 109
Bion, W. R. 8, 15, 17–18, 20, 27, 43, 57, 74, 76, 98; beta elements 109; containment 123; reverie 110
bizarre objects 18
blame 135
bodies, relationships with 107, 118–20; chronic physical conditions, emotional impacts 111–15; mourning loss of disability 115–16; sado-masochistic relationships with 116–18; stomach issues 107–11
borderline personality disorder see EUPD (emotionally unstable personality disorder)
breakdown of illusions, suicide 52–3
breakdowns 34
Britton, R. 17, 75, 77, 124
Bronstein, C. 84

Campbell, D. 54, 60
capacity for reverie 15
CBT (cognitive behavioural therapy) 2
challenges, of treating EUPD 78–9
chronic physical conditions, emotional impacts 111–15
clinical leadership 127–8, 136
clinical staff, support for 6–7
clinical supervision 64
clinician-patient relationships, target culture 130–2
clinicians, pressure on 55–8
cognitive behavioural therapy (CBT) 2
collapse of illusions 53–5
common mental disorders 1–2
communication: concrete communication 71, 91; psychotic communications see psychotic communications; symbolic communication 71; unconscious communications 35
concrete communication 71–3, 91
concrete thinking, symbolisation and 17
containment 15–16, 123; in-patient units 87–91
core complex 54, 77
counter-transference 9–11, 91; EUPD (emotionally unstable personality disorder) 80; therapeutic relationships 41–3
Crohn's disease 118; emotional impact 111–15

daydreams 37
delusions: assault on sanity 84–6; as defence against depressive breakdown and fragmentation 86–7; symbolic thinking 83–4
denial 25–6

dependence 35, 45
depression 3–4; post-natal depression 96;
    projection of 96–9; suicidality 60–3
depressive breakdowns, delusions 86–7
depressive positions 12–13, 67, 123;
    containment 16
depressive states 57
despair 4
differentiating between health and illness
    24–5
disabilities, mourning loss of 115–16
discharge 3; early discharge 5
double bookkeeping 85
dreams 91
drug use 96–7

early discharge 5
ego 8–9, 107
ego destructive super ego 98
emotion impact of chronic physical
    conditions 111–15
emotionally unstable personality disorder
    (EUPD) 66–7, 125; challenges of
    treating 78–9; concrete communication
    71–3; counter-transference 80;
    paranoid-schizoid position 67–71;
    search for supportive relationships 73–5;
    separation from tyrannical internal
    figures 76–8
empathy, lack of 132
eradicating psychosis 29–30
EUPD (emotionally unstable personality
    disorder) 66–7, 125; challenges of
    treating 78–9; concrete communication
    71–3; counter-transference 80;
    paranoid-schizoid position 67–71;
    search for supportive relationships 73–5;
    separation from tyrannical internal
    figures 76–8
exoskeletons 104
external objects 39
external relationships 69

Fabricius, J. 134
father figures 111
feelings of despair 4
fragmentation, delusions 86–7
Francis, Lord 6, 121, 129–30, 132, 137
Freud, S. 3, 57, 59, 91; counter-
    transference 9–11; ego 107; Oedipus
    complex 16–17; repetition compulsion
    54; structural theory of the mind

8–9; transference 9–11, 37; traumatic
    situations 104
funding for mental health services 31

good mother 16, 122–3
guilt 13–14

Hale, R. 54
Halton, W. 132
health, differentiating between health and
    illness 24–5
health care systems 137; austerity
    measures 129–30; internal market
    128–9; see also institutions
Heimann, P. 10
humiliation 4, 23, 40–1

IAPT (Increasing Access to Psychological
    Treatment) services 2
id 8–9
idealisation 99–100
identifications 124–5
illness, differentiating between health and
    illness 24–5
illusions: breakdown of 52–3; collapse of
    53–5
Increasing Access to Psychological
    Treatment (IAPT) services 2
infants 11–12; abandonment 95;
    dependence 11, 15–16; mother-infant
    relationship 46, 74–5; paranoid-schizoid
    position 14–15; primary objects 73
in-patient units, as containers to help
    patients bear psychic pain 87–91
insight 35
institutional support 126
institutions: austerity measures 129–30;
    fragmentation of authority 127–8;
    historical examples 126–7; nurse-
    patient relationships see nurse-patient
    relationships; target culture 130–2
internal gangs 41–2, 86, 117
internal market, of health care system 128–9
internal narcissistic gang 19
internal objects 57–8, 103

Jacques, E. 124
Joseph, B. 41, 77

Klein, M. 11, 73, 122; depressive
    positions 12, 67, 95–6, 123; external
    objects 39; idealisation 100; manic

reparation 13–14; manic state of mind 12–13; paranoid-schizoid position 11–12, 67, 123; projection of depression 96–9; projective identification 14–15; reparation 13–14; transference 37

leadership 126, 136
Lucas, R. 7, 57, 79, 91; exoskeletons 104; manic state of mind 103

magical thinking 37
management, relationships with 6
manic depressive defence 94–5
manic reparation 13–14, 96, 104
manic state of mind 12–13
markets, internal market 128–9
Marty, P. 107
masochistic state of mind 3
medication, anti-psychotic medication 3
melancholia 3
mental health policy 1–2
mental health professionals 4–5; relationship with management 6; support for 6–7
mental health services 31–2
mental health teams 35
Menzies Lyth, I. 124, 126–7, 132–3, 136
Mid Staffs Foundation Trust 121–2
Minne, C. 104
Money-Kyrle, R. 10
morale 6
mother-infant relationship 110; dependence, 11; good mother/bad mother 122–3
mourning loss of disability in therapy 115–16
M'Uzan, M. 107

non-psychotic parts of the mind 17–19, 26–8
nurse training institutions 133
nurse-patient relationships 112; fragmentation of authority 127–8; historical example 126–7
nurses: leadership and institutional support 126; therapeutic settings 124–5; training 121–2, 132–5

objects 9
Oedipal triangle, symbolic thinking 16–17
O'Shaughnessy, E. 7, 61
over identification 39

"package of care" system 129
paranoid-schizoid position 11–13, 90, 123; EUPD (emotionally unstable personality disorder) 67–71
parasuicide 50; collapse of illusions 53–5; pressure on clinicians to be the ideal object 55–8; pre-suicidal state 52–3; therapeutic engagement 51–2; unconscious phantasy in therapeutic relationships 58–60; see also suicide
patient-centred interpretations 79
personality disorder 67; see also EUPD (emotionally unstable personality disorder)
PICU (Psychiatric Intensive Care Unit) 84–5
post-natal depression 96–8
post-traumatic depression 86
pressure on clinicians to be the ideal object 55–8
pre-suicidal state 52–3
Project 2000 133–4
projection 47
projection of depression 96–9
projective identification 14–15; therapeutic relationships 39–41
Psychiatric Intensive Care Unit (PICU) 84–5
psychic retreat 19
psychoanalytic model 32
psychosis 30–1; attempts at eradicating 29–30
psychotic 5
psychotic communications 82–3; assault on sanity 84–6; breakdown in symbolic thinking 83–4; delusions as defence against depressive breakdowns and fragmentation 86–7; in-patient units 87–91; therapeutic relationships 43–6
psychotic defences 20, 36
psychotic internal gang 41–2
psychotic parts of the mind 17–19, 26–8
psychotic patient, attack on sanity 28–9
psychotic states of mind 1

rationalisation 25–6
relationships: with bodies see bodies, relationships with; external relationships 69; with management 6; mother-infant relationship 110; nurse-patient relationships see nurse-patient relationships; sado-masochistic

relationships with the body 116–18; search for supportive relationships, EUPD 73–5; special relationships 69
reparation 13–14, 96
repetition compulsion 54
repetitive acting out, treatment-resistant patients 100–2
responding to psychotic forces, in counter-transference 41–3
Revans, R. 132
reverie 20, 110
Rey, H. 70, 76; internal objects, 103
Rosenfeld, H. 19, 41, 69, 86, 117

sado-masochistic relationships with the body 116–19
sanity, psychotic communications 84–6
secondary mental health services 2
Segal, H. 11, 17, 71, 110; symbolic equation 123
self-awareness 35
self-harming behaviour 67, 117
separation from tyrannical internal figures, EUPD (emotionally unstable personality disorder) 76–8
severe mental illness 1
sexualisation 97
shame 23
Sifneos, P. E. 107
social systems 122–4; austerity measures 129–30; internal market 128–9; target culture 130–2; therapeutic settings 124–5; leadership and support 125–8; training nurses 132–5
Sohn, L. 83
special relationships 69
splitting 12, 67
staff 6, 31–3; Oedipal triangle 17; psychiatric settings 103–5; see also nurses
states of chronic suicidality 60–3
Steiner, J. 19, 22, 62, 79–80; idealisation 100
Stekel, W. 57
stomach issues 118; bodies, relationships with 107–111
structural theory of the mind (Freud) 8–9
student nurses, training of 132–5
suicidal phantasies 54

suicidality 60–3
suicide 50; risk of 50–1; states of chronic suicidality 60–3; therapeutic engagement 51–2; unconscious phantasy 58–60; see also parasuicide
super ego 8–9
supervision groups 44–5, 47, 92
support for clinical staff 6–7
supportive relationships, EUPD (emotionally unstable personality disorder) 73–5
survival anxiety 135
symbolic communication 71
symbolic equation 123
symbolic reparation 104
symbolic thinking: Oedipal triangle 16–17; psychotic communications 83–4
symbolisation, concrete thinking and 17

target culture 130–2
teams 136
therapeutic engagement, parasuicide 51–2
therapeutic relationships 34–7; counter-transference 41–3; over identification 39; projective identification 39–41; psychotic communications 43–6; transference enactment 37–9; unconscious phantasy 58–60
therapeutic settings 124–5
therapists 37
training for nurses 121–2, 132–5
transference 9–11
transference enactment, therapeutic relationships 37–9
traumatic situations 104
treatment-resistant patients 94; idealisation 99–100; manic depressive defence 94–5; repetitive acting out 100–2
trigger factors 52
tryannical internal figures, separation from (EUPD) 76–8

unconscious communications 35
unconscious phantasy 9; therapeutic relationships 58–60

Winnicott, D. W. 46

zero tolerance, suicide 50